Probabilistic Characterization of Soil Properties:

Bridge Between Theory and Practice

Proceedings of a symposium sponsored by the
ASCE Geotechnical Engineering Division
in conjunction with the ASCE Convention
in Atlanta, Georgia
May 17, 1984

Edited by David S. Bowles and Hon-Yim Ko

Published by the
American Society of Civil Engineers
345 East 47th Street
New York, New York 10017-2398

Copyright © 1984 by the American Society of Civil Engineers,
All Rights Reserved.
Library of Congress Catalog Card No. 84-70572
ISBN 0-87262-398-X
Manufactured in the United States of America.

PREFACE

This book contains papers that were presented at a one day symposium held at the National Convention of the American Society of Civil Engineers on May 17, 1984 in Atlanta, Georgia. The symposium, which was entitled, "Probabilistic Characterization of Soil Properties," was jointly sponsored by the Safety and Reliability Committee and the Soil Properties Committee of the Geotechnical Engineering Division of ASCE.

Two objectives were established for the symposium, as follows:

1. To summarize the principles and procedures of probabilistic characterization of soil properties in a readily understood manner rather than a highly theoretical treatment.

2. To present examples of the applications of probabilistic characterization in the form of case studies.

In short, the symposium was intended to be a "bridge between theory and practice."

Consistent with these objectives, the symposium was divided into two parts: the state-of-the-art and case studies. Four eminent geotechnical engineers were invited to summarize the state-of-the-art in probabilistic characterization of soil properties in the morning session. The afternoon session comprised several case studies contributed by engineers in practice and in research. Each of the papers in the case studies part of the Proceedings has received two positive peer reviews. Each of the state-of-the-art papers has been accepted by the Proceedings Editors. All papers are eligible for discussion in the Journal of Geotechnical Engineering Division. All papers are eligible for ASCE awards.

We wish to thank the authors and the reviewers for their efforts in producing high quality manuscripts for presentation at the symposium and for inclusion in this book. Also we wish to thank Shiela Menaker, Manager, Book Production, ASCE, for her excellent work in arranging for the production of this book.

We trust that this book will be helpful to geotechnical practitioners and researchers who are interested in using probabilistic methods in geotechnical engineering.

David S. Bowles

Hon-Yim Ko

TABLE OF CONTENTS

Part I: State-of-the-art

Part II: Case Studies

"Just A Few More Tests and We'll be Sure!"

Gregory B. Baecher, A.M., ASCE*

Geotechnical engineering, once a field dominated by craftsmen has developed during the past decades into an engineering discipline based on mathematical modeling, sophisticated physical testing, and other hallmarks of scientific method. One of the last areas of geotechnical engineering to benefit from this rationalization is data analysis and site characterization. These are still approached heuristicaly, with little advantage taken of modern concepts of data analysis common in engineering and science.

The slow introduction of modern data analysis into geotechnical practice is not without cause or wholly unjustified. The very nature of site characterization is based on familiarity with geology, with experience, and with intuition. Geological exploration at its foundation is an inductive enterprise. Nothing the analyst, scientist, or engineer can do will change this fact. The "rational" methods of statistics and operations research shed little light on the most basic problems of interpreting geological history.

On the other hand, to say that scientific methods have limitations is not to say they are useless. It is true that fundamental aspects of site characterization are outside the purview of 'analysis'--statistical or otherwise--yet, current geotechnical practice is based on predictive modeling and thus requires that data be interpreted quantitativly. Here, within this confined space, scientific data analysis provides three benefits: (i) new insights, (ii) predictions that were hitherto impossible, and (iii) greater efficiency.

This short paper presents a practical approach to data analysis, with the intent of suggesting that simple statistical methods--when tailored to geotechnical problems--do in fact provide benefits. The first section following outlines a simple approach to analyzing site characterization data. Then to be specific, three examples are used to illustrate the ease of applying improved data analysis techniques and benefits accruing to those who do. The examples focus on three questions:

* Associate Professor of Civil Engineering, Massachusetts Institute of Technology, Cambridge, MA 02139

- How to distinguish real variability of soil properties from measurement "noise?"

- How to select design parameters from scattered data?

- How to assess the reliability of calculations and select factors of safety?

'SCIENTIFIC' DATA ANALYSIS

'Scientific' data anlysis in the sense used here means a rational approach to evaluating and understanding (i) the scatter observed in field or laboratory data, and (ii) systematic errors which affect engineering predictions. The procedure outlined is simple; it is no more than error analysis, and its mathematics are trivial.

Algebra of Error Propagation

The simplest description of an error or uncertain variable is by its mean and standard deviation. The mean is simply the arithmetical average and is taken as the 'best estimate' of a variable, e.g., from a set of data $\underline{z} = (z_1, ..., z_n)$ the mean is,

$$E[z] = \frac{1}{n} \Sigma z_i = \text{"mean"} \qquad . \qquad (1)$$

The standard deviation is the square root of the average squared variability (variance),

$$V[z] = \frac{1}{n-1} \Sigma (z_i - E[z])^2 = \text{"variance"} \quad , \qquad (2)$$

$$SD[z] = \sqrt{V[z]} = \text{"standard deviation"} \quad , \qquad (3)$$

and is taken as the 'uncertainty' about the best estimate. The proportional uncertainty normalized by the mean is said to be the coefficient of variation

$$\Omega[z] = SD[z]/E[z] = \text{"coefficient of variation"} . \qquad (4)$$

The association between the uncertainties of two variables z and y is usually expressed by their covariance,

$$C[z_i, z_j] = \frac{1}{n-1} \Sigma (z_i - E[z_i])(z_j - E[z_j]) \qquad . \qquad (5)$$

If y is a scalar depending on a vector of uncertain parameters through the function (i.e., model)

$$y = g(\underline{z}) \quad ; \tag{6}$$

then as a linear approximation,

$$E[y] \simeq g(E[\underline{z}]) \tag{7}$$

or just the common deterministic solution, and

$$V[y] \simeq \sum_{i=1}^{n} \sum_{j=1}^{n} \frac{\partial g(\underline{z})}{\partial z_i} \frac{\partial g(\underline{z})}{\partial z_j} C[z_i, z_j] \tag{8}$$

in which $C[z_i, z_i] = V[z_i]$ (see Appendix for general result).

Two useful special cases of Eqn. 8 are for the additive function,

$$y = a + b_i z_i \quad \Rightarrow \quad V[y] \simeq \sum b_i^2 V[z_i] \tag{9}$$

and for the multiplicative function,

$$y = \Pi \, b_i z_i^{c_i} \quad \Rightarrow \quad \Omega^2[y] \simeq \sum c_i^2 \, \Omega^2[z_i] \tag{10}$$

in which Ω = "coefficient of variation" = mean/standard deviation.

Data Scatter

The scatter of geotechnical data derives from two sources, soil variability and measurement error. Since these have differing effects on predictions, efficiency can be gained by separating them.

The undrained strength profile of Fig. 1 can be used to illustrate the the difference between soil variability and measurement error. This figure shows aggregated field vane data measured in a soft clay deposit along the axes of a proposed embankment [1].

Lacking contrary observations, the vane strengths are assumed to vary systematically with depth but not

horizontally. An adequate model of data scatter is then
obtained by presuming soil variability and measurement error
to be additive,

$$z = x + \varepsilon \quad , \tag{11}$$

in which z=field vane strength, x="actual" undrained
strength, and ε=random measurement error. Then the variance
of field vane strengths is related to the variances of
spatial variability and measurment error from Eqn. 7 as,

$$V[z] = V[x] + V[\varepsilon] \quad , \tag{12}$$

in which measurement bias is ignored. Unfortunately though,
barring further analysis one does not know how the data
scatter variance of Fig. 1 is divided between soil
variability and measurement error.

Soil Variability

In principle, with a
sufficient number of
measurements, soil
properties at every point in
the subsurface could be
known within the accuracy of
testing. Practically,
however, this is not
possible. Soil properties
are known only at points and
must be interpolated
between.

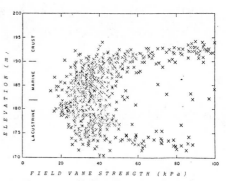

F I E L D   V A N E   S T R E N G T H   (k P a)

Figure 1 -- Field vane strength data for a soft clay
profile showing considerable data scatter.

For the purpose of this
interpolation spatial
variation is conveniently
divided into two terms, a
smoothly varying trend and
local deviations about the
trend. Thus, z at some
point in space $\underline{a}$, where $\underline{a}$ is
the vector of location
coordinates, is expressed as

$$z(\underline{a}) = t(\underline{a}) + u(\underline{a}) \tag{13}$$

in which $t(\underline{a})$ is the trend
component at $\underline{a}$, and $u(\underline{a})$ is
the deviation from the trend
at $\underline{a}$ (Figure 2). For
convenience, the magnitude
of these deviations from the

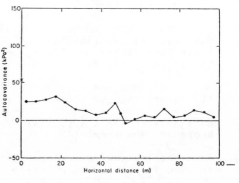

Figure 2 -- Horizontal autocovariance
function for the FV data of Fig. 1.

trend can be expressed as a variance $V[u]$ or standard deviation $SD[u]$.

If z is a continuous variable and the soil deposit is zonally homogeneous, then at locations close together the deviations $u(\underline{a}_i)$ and $u(\underline{a}_j)$ should be expected to be similar. Indeed, as the separation approaches zero, $u(\underline{a}_i)$ and $u(\underline{a}_j)$ become identical. Conversely, at locations widely separated the deviations should not be expected to be similar. This spatial association between deviations off the trend $t(\underline{a})$ can be summarized by a function describing the similarity of $u(\underline{a}_i)$ and $u(\underline{a}_j)$ as the distance $r=|\underline{a}_i-\underline{a}_j|$ increases. One such function is the autocovariance

$$C(\underline{r}) = E[u(\underline{a}_i) \cdot u(\underline{a}_j)]$$

$$= E[\{z(\underline{a}_i)-t(\underline{a}_i)\}\{z(\underline{a}_j)-t(\underline{a}_j)\}] \quad . \tag{14}$$

This function is assumed the same in every part of an homogeneous zone of soil, which is simply to assume that the soil is 'statistically homogeneous'. Clearly, when i=j the deviations become identical, and $C(0)=V[u]$.

For the data of Fig. 1, an estimate of the horizontal autocovariance function is shown as Fig. 2. 4. It is important to emphasize that the autocovariance function is an artifact of the way one models soil variability. There is nothing innate about the chosen trend $t(\underline{a})$, and changing the trend necessarily changes $C(\underline{r})$.

Random Measurement Error

Random measurement error--"noise"--is presumed to be independent from one test to another, to have mean zero, $E[\varepsilon]=0$ and to have everywhere the same standard deviation, $SD[\varepsilon]=\sqrt{V[\varepsilon]}$. A non-zero-mean error is treated as a bias.

Random measurement error can be estimated in a number of ways, for example by replicate testing or multiple profiling, but a convenient way is through the autocovarince function. Returning to Eqns. 9 and 11, field vane strengths are represented as

$$z(\underline{a}) = t(\underline{a}) + u(\underline{a}) + \varepsilon(\underline{a}) \quad . \tag{15}$$

The autocovariance of (7), after the trend has been removed, becomes

$$C_z(\underline{r}) = C_x(\underline{r}) + C_\varepsilon(\underline{r}) \quad , \tag{16}$$

in which $C_x(\underline{a})$ is from Eqn. 12, and $C_\varepsilon(\underline{r})$ is the autocovariance function of ε. Since $\varepsilon(\underline{a}_i)$ and $\varepsilon(\underline{a}_j)$ are independent except for i=j, the autocovariance function of ε

is a spike at r=0 and zero
otherwise. Thus, $C_z(\underline{r})$ is as
shown in Fig. 3. By
extrapolating observed
autocovariances to the origin,
one obtains an estimate of the
fraction of data scatter
coming from random error (or
very small scale soil
variability). For the data of
Fig. 2, $V[\epsilon] \approx 0.45 V[z]$.

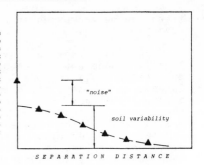

Figure 3 -- Manifestation of random measurement
error ('noise') in autocovariance function.

Statistical Uncertainty

Because a limited number of measurements are made at
any depth, about 27 in Fig. 1, their average may be above or
below the actual spatial average even if there were no
measurement bias. Therefore the estimate of average vane
strength at any depth shown in Fig. 1 is probably somewhat
in error, and to the extent that it is, this error is the
same everywhere along the axis; it is systematic.

The larger the number of measurement at any depth, the
lower one might expect this error to be. From rudimentary
statistics, the magnitude of this error as a first
approximation, is

$$V[\hat{E}[x]] \quad \simeq \quad \{\frac{1}{n}\}^t \underline{C} \quad \{\frac{1}{n}\} \tag{17}$$

in which $\{1/n\}$ is a vector of dimension n, each element of
which is $1/n$, and $\underline{C}$ is the covariance matrix of the
observations. That is, $\underline{C}$ is the nxn matrix each element of
which is the value of the autocovariance function evaluated
for the separation distance of the i and j measurements. If
the measurements are widely spaced, Eqn. 17 reduces to

$$V[\hat{E}[z]] = \frac{V[z]}{n} \tag{18}$$

in which "^" means an estimate, here of the mean.

Bias Error

Systematic error is also introduced by the method of
measurement and this error is called measurement bias.
Since variations in bias from one test to another may be
lumped with random error, bias does not appear in the data
scatter.

In most cases there is little reason to separate measurement bias from model uncertainty. Indeed, one could argue that there is no distinction. Models are used to predict the behavior of a physical system and are always simplifications. The parameters used as input to a model are no more than calibration factors. Because the model is an abstraction there is no such thing as an "innate" soil property. All soil properties are simply those which cause a model to best fit empirical observations. For example, soil is not an elastic continuum and therefore deformation modulus E cannot be innate. E is estimated for a particular soil only in order that an elastic analysis might accurately mimic observed deformations.

The most direct way to establish measurement bias is by comparing predicted and observed performance. For field vane strengths Bjerrum [2] compared observed slope performance with predictions based on modified Bishop analysis, and backcalculated the correction factor $\mu=[c_u$ for FS=1 at failure/ $c_u(FV)]$ reconciling observed failures with predictions (Fig. 4). This bias factor inexorably combines measurement technique and prediction model and no longer obtains if a stability model based on other assumptions is used.

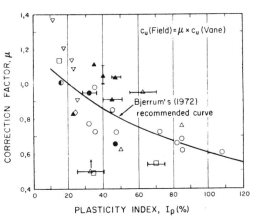

Figure 4 -- Bjerrum's correction factor for field vane strength (from Ladd, et al, 1977).

Introducing a measurement/model bias B into Eqn. 9 leads to the statistical model,

$$z = Bx + \varepsilon ,\qquad(19)$$

and the summation of variances,

$$V[z] = B^2 V[x] + x^2 V[B] + V[\varepsilon] ,\qquad(20)$$

in which $V[B]$ is the uncertainty in the value of the bias correction B, and all parameters are valued at their means.

In the special case of FV measurements used in modified Bishop analysis, $B=(1/\mu)$.

Data Analysis Procedure

The contributions of these sources of data scatter and error to estimates of soil properties at any point is found by rearranging the terms of Eqn. 17 and applying Eqn. 8 to obtain,

$$V[x] \approx \frac{1}{B^2} \ (V[z]-V[\varepsilon]) \ + \ z^2 \ V[\frac{1}{B}] \ + \ V[\hat{E}[z]] \qquad (21)$$

$$= \ \text{spatial variance} \ \} \ \text{soil variability}$$
$$+$$
$$\text{measurement bias}$$
$$+ \qquad \qquad \} \ \text{systematic error}$$
$$\text{systematic error}$$

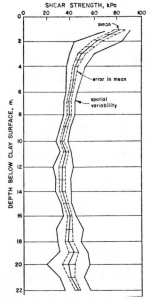

SHEAR STRENGTH, kPa

DEPTH BELOW CLAY SURFACE, m.

mean

error in mean

spatial variability

Figure 5 -- Best estimate of strength profile with spatial and systematic error standard deviation envelopes.

The contribution of random measurement error appears only in its effect on statistical error. This means that $V[x]$ can in specific instances be considerably less than the data scatter variance $V[z]$.

In separating spatial variability and systematic error, it is easiest to think of spatial variation as scatter about the trend and to think of systematic error as a uncertainty on the trend itself. The first type envelope in Fig. 5 is due only to soil variability after random measurement error is removed. The second type envelope is due to statistical error and measurement bias.

Because uncertainty comprises both spatial and systematic components, the magnitude of uncertainty which must be dealt with depends on the volume of soil mobilized in the limiting state. For large volumes of soil and limiting states that depend on average properties, the spatial component of variability averages out. For small volumes (→0), this component contributes in its full magnitude to uncertainty. On the other hand, for limiting states that depend on extreme elements of soil (e.g., progressive failure, piping), the spatial component of variability

becomes increasingly important as the volume of soil
mobilized becomes larger. Therefore, a variance multipler R
typically augments the first term of the RHS of Eqn. 21.
The magnitude of R depends on the limiting state and the
volume of soil, the latter depending on the distance to
which significant autocorrelations exist.

Factors of Safety

The choice of factors of safety for design nominally
reflects a balancing of (i) the cost of achieving a given
FS, against (ii) the uncertainty of performance predictions
and the consequences of inadequate performance. From an
engineering as opposed to economic view, however, one
desires primarily that FS's be consistent, in the sense that
FS's should imply similar levels of safety.

When geotechnical data are analyzed to estimate
variances as well as means, the traditional point estimate
of FS is replaced by a mean and standard deviation of FS.
These may be combined at the simplest level in a
(first-order) reliability index

$$\beta = \frac{E[FS] - 1.0}{SD[FS]} = \text{"Reliability Index"} \tag{22}$$

which is the normalized distance between the mean FS (i.e.,
best estimate) and the nominal failure value (1.0) in
standard deviation units. E.g., $\beta=2$ means that the best
estimate of FS is 2 standard deviations away from the
limiting value. The index β is not without deficiencies,
but it is more complete than the point estimate of FS alone.

The standard deviation on FS established in this way
pertains to engineering calculations, not physical reality.

Whether a facility performs adequately is deterministically related to its design and geological conditions. The uncertainty lies in limited information about physical reality. Uncertainty in FS has to do with the chance that, if the proper analysis had been made and if the proper parameter values had been used, then the predicted FS would have been less than 1.0. Thus, in the present context one appropriately speaks of the reliability of a prediction, not the reliability of a facility.

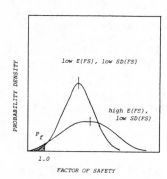

Figure 6 -- The reliability of a calculation depends both on the mean and on the standard deviation.

As Fig. 6 shows, the reliability of a prediction is not completely described by E[FS] alone. A high E[FS] combined with a high SD[FS] may be a less reliable prediction than a low E[FS] combined with a low SD[FS]. The reliability index β captures this distinction.

The choice of design factors of safety for different conditions can be made consistent, in that the same level of reliability is implied, by setting the corresponding reliability indices equal. As shown in Fig. 7, for two design cases in which the coefficients of variation of calculated FS's are 0.10 and 0.20, respectively, the β's corresponding to design (expected) FS's of 1.5 are $\beta_{0.10} = 3.33$ and $\beta_{0.20} = 1.67$. To obtain FS's implying consistent reliability, at say β=2, the target values would have to be $FS_{0.10} = 1.25$ and $FS_{0.20} = 1.67$, respectively. Thus, β is a vehicle for selecting consistent criteria.

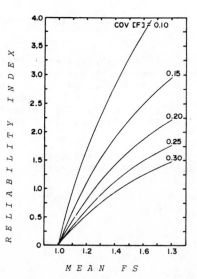

Figure 7 -- Reliability index as a function of E(FS) and coefficient of variation of FS.

MEASUREMENT NOISE AND ITS EFFECTS

The importance of random measurement errors in soil data is well illustrated in a case investigated by Hilldale-Cuningham [4] involving the settlement of shallow footings on a uniform sand. The site overlies approximately ten meters of uniform wind-blown sand, on which a large number of footings were constructed for an industrial facility. Great care was taken to characterize the site by Standard Penetration blow count measurements and to predict and then measure subsequent settlements [3].

A review of measured blow counts and measured settlements reveals an interesting discrepancy. Since footing settlements on sand are approximately proportional to the inverse of average blow count in the zone immediately beneath the footing, one should expect from Eqn. 10 that the coefficient of variation of the settlements would be approximately that of the vertically averaged blow counts. Mathematically, settlement is predicted by a formula of the form,

$$\rho \propto \frac{\Delta q}{N} \, g(B) \quad , \tag{23}$$

in which ρ=maximum settlement, Δq=net applied stress at the base of the footing, N=average corrected blow count, and g(B)=a function of footing width. Therefore,

$$\Omega[P] \simeq \Omega[N] \quad ; \tag{24}$$

but, it does not. The coefficient of variation of the vertically averaged blow counts is about 0.50 (Fig. 8); the coefficient of variation of the settlements is only 0.37 (Fig. 9). Why the difference?

Perhaps the best explanation of this apparent inconsistency is found in estimates of measurement noise in the blow count data. Fig. 10 shows the horizontal autocorrelation function estimated by Hilldale-Cunningham for the blow count data. By extrapolating this function to the origin, the noise (or high frequency) content of the data is estimated to be about 50% of the data scatter variance. This means that,

$$(\Omega_{soil})^2 = (\Omega_{data})^2 \, (0.5)$$
$$= (0.35)^2 \tag{25}$$

which is remarkably--and perhaps coincidentally--close to the observed variability of the settlements. Measurement noise of 50% or even more of the observed scatter of in situ test data, particularly the SPT, have been observed on several projects (e.g., [6]).

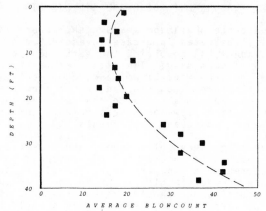

Figure 8 -- Average standard penetration test blow count data showing trend with depth.

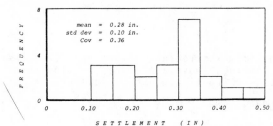

Figure 9 -- Histogram of footing settlement showing a coefficient of variation of about 0.36.

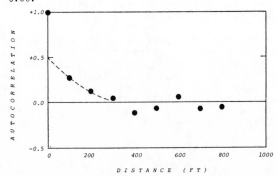

Figure 10 -- Autocorrelation of SPT blow count data of Fig. 8, showing a contribution of about 50% of the data scatter from noise (after Hilldale-Cunningham, 1971).

SEPARATING SOURCES OF ERROR

The differing influence of different sources of uncertainty is well illustrated by a second case involving an ore stockpile on soft clay.

The facility is an industrial plant sited along a barge canal on approximately 15 m of normally consolidated marine clay. Ores for processing are shipped up the canal and stock piled next to a docking facility. For operational reasons it is desirable to build these stock piles to about 12 m. However, the clay cannot support this load, necessitating staged construction.

Strength data for the site are scattered (Fig. 11), as are maximum pressure measurements (Fig. 12). This leads to considerable uncertainty in predicted factors of safety against strength instability, and thus to uncertainty on how high the embankments can be built before strength increases from consolidation are necessary for further construction. 'Scientific' data analysis was called on to answer two questions: (1) how does the data scatter affect uncertainties in the estimated strength profile, and (2) what risks would have to be accepted as the embankment is raised?

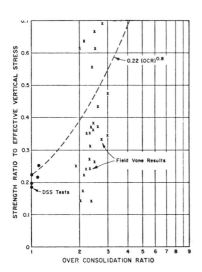

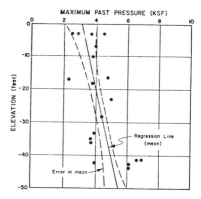

Figure 12 -- Maximum past pressure data showing trend with depth and statistical error (SD) on trend.

Figure 11 -- Field vane data plotted against OCR (data from Norie, 1982).

Since the field vane data were too sparce to
confidently estimate measurement noise, stability
predictions were based on normalized properties and the
results of laboratory tests. By so doing, a limited number
of tests on high quality specimens can substitute for a
large number of less precise measurements such as field
vanes.

The SHANSEP procedure [5] relates undrained strength c_u
to in situ vertical effective stress through the function,

$$\frac{c_u}{\sigma'_{vo}} = k \, [OCR]^m \tag{26}$$

in which $k=[C_u/\sigma'_{vm}]_{NC}$ (i.e., a material constant), OCR=over
consolidation ratio, and m=a material constant. Applying
Eqn. 10

$$\Omega^2[C_u] \simeq \Omega^2[k] + m^2\Omega^2[\sigma'_m] + \ln^2(\sigma'_m/\sigma'_{vo}) \, V[m], \tag{27}$$

providing a linear composition of the uncertainties on each
of the three soil parameters, k,m, and σ'_m.

The means and standard deviations of k and m are taken
from laboratory direct simple shear tests. Statistical
uncertainty is estimated by Eqn. 18. The mean trend of σ'_m
with depth was estimated by regression analysis, from which
statistical error in the trend line follows. Fig. 13 shows
the corresponding best estimate profile and its spatial and
systematic error bands.

The various standard deviation envelopes apply
respectively to limiting states mobilizing various soil
volumes from small to large. The uncertainty remaining for
infinitely large soil volumes results from systematic error
and cannot be reduced without further testing. First-order
reliability indices are shown in Fig. 14 as a function of
stockpile height.

The distinction between soil variability and systematic
error on this project is important. Soil variability leads
to local failures, because locally a pocket of soil may be
weak. Systematic error leads to total failures because
estimates of soil strength may be wholly erroneous.
Simultaneously, uncertainty due to soil variability may not
be reduced without detailed trend maps, something difficult
to construct and use. On the other hand, systematic errors
may be reduced by increased sample sizes or by improved
calibration. Careful data analysis on this project provided
insight on the implications of large data scatter for design

parameters, and it provided a means for selecting factors of
safety in balance with those parameter estimates.

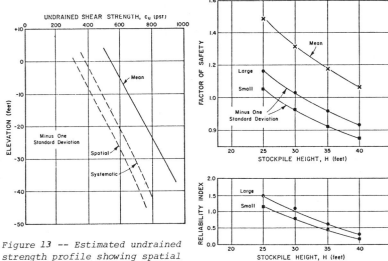

Figure 13 -- Estimated undrained
strength profile showing spatial
and systematic SD envelopes.

Figure 14 -- Calculated FS as a function
of stockpile height, showing SD's and
reliability indices.

BALANCING FACTORS OF SAFETY

The effect of differing levels of uncertainty on
comparitive factors of safety is illustrated by returning to
the project from which the field vane data of Section 2 have
come. This project also involved staged construction of a
dyke on soft clay. The first stage was to be constructed to
a height of about 12 m, and then after partial consolidation
the second stage was to be constructed to about 25 m.
Consolidation was to be accelerated using wick drains and
then monitored with piezometers.

Upon first inspection a natural presumption is that the
second stage construction should be designed more conservatively than the first, for at least two reasons: The consequences of failure of the higher dyke are presumably
larger, and less experience has accumulated on this particular clay with high embankments. This presumption leads to
the conclusion that the design FS against foundation instability should be higher for the higher dyke than for the

first stage dyke. However, the presumption may be overly
conservative.

     Table 1 shows the variance composition for the FS
against foundation instability of a typical first stage
design. The stability calculations were made with both
Modified Bishop and Morgenstern-Price methods assuming
undrained failure based on FV strengths. Table 2 shows the
analogous variance composition for a typical second stage
design. The analysis was based on normalized UD strength
parameters and increases in σ'_{vc} at various degrees of
consolidation (as monitored by piezometers). In fact,
because the normalized strength parameters and changes in
effective stress can be known more precisely than can
existing UD strengths, the reliability of the predictions
for the second stage (high) dyke is greater than the
corresponding reliability for the first stage (low) dyke.
Therefore, consistent reliability in the sense of similar
β's is achieved by adopting a greater design FS for the low
dyke than for the high dyke. For example, to achieve $\beta=2$
for the first stage requires FS=1.34, whereas for the second
stage requires only FS=1.23. However, since the
consequences of failures of the latter are more severe and
since unforeseen phenomena may be also be more important for
the latter, a reasonable strategy is perhaps to use the same
design FS for both cases.

                        CONCLUSIONS

     Modern data analysis techniques provide a rational
means for dealing with data scatter, sample size effects,
and measurement bias when evaluating site characterization
data. Specifically, they allow random measurement errors to
be removed from data scatter and they provide a means for
selecting design parameters and design factors of safety
which are consistent with each other. Inspection alone does
not allow these capabilities.

                     ACKNOWLEDGEMENTS

The author wishes to gratefully acknowledge the influence of
Charles C. Ladd on the ideas contained in this paper, and
for providing the opportunity to collaborate on projects
involving soft clay construction.

Parameter	$\Delta F/\Delta x_i$	Variance Systematic	Variance TOTAL	$(\Delta F/\Delta x_i)^2 \cdot V(x_i)$ Systematic	$(\Delta F/\Delta x_i)^2 \cdot V(x_i)$ TOTAL
φ'	0.01	3.0	4.0	0.0003	0.0004
YFILL	0.06	1.0	2.0	0.0036	0.0072
Dcrust	0.008	0.036	1.0	---	0.0013
Dtill	0.056	1.0	1.0	0.0031	0.0031
$c_u(L)$	0.0215	24.9	99.7	0.0115	0.0461
$c_u(M)$	0.0137	7.6	47.6	0.0014	0.0089

$$V[F] = 0.0199 \quad 0.0670$$
$$SD[F] = 0.141 \quad 0.259$$
$$V_{125\phi}[F] = 0.0199 \quad 0.0094$$

$$\beta = \frac{1.453 - 1.0}{\sqrt{0.029}} = 2.66$$

Table 1 -- Variance composition of the single stage (12m) dyke showing contributions of various uncertainties to the SD(FS) and reliability index.

Parameter	$\Delta F/\Delta x_i$	Variance Systematic	Variance TOTAL	$(\Delta F/\Delta x_i)^2 \cdot V(x_i)$ Systematic $\times 10^{-4}$	$(\Delta F/\Delta x_i)^2 \cdot V(x_i)$ TOTAL $\times 10^{-4}$
Intact					
τ(M)	0.0018	13.3	41.5	nil	1
τ(L)	0.012	26.3	88.5	38	127
Consolidated					
τ(M)	0.0021	52.7	111.5	2.3	4.9
τ(L)	0.009	62.0	124.4	50	101
φ	0.0088	3.0	4.0	2	3
YFILL	0.055	1.0	2.0	30	61

$$V[F] = 0.0122 \quad 0.0298$$
$$SD[F] = 0.111 \quad 0.173$$
$$V_{ave}[F] = 0.0122 + 0.0012 = 0.0134$$

$$\beta = \frac{1.427 - 1.0}{\sqrt{0.0134}} = 3.68$$

Table 2 -- Variance composition of the two stage dyke (24m) showing contributions of various uncertainties to SD(FS) and reliability index.

REFERENCES

[1] Baecher, G.B., "Simplified geotechnical data analysis,"
NATO Advanced Study Institute on Structural and Geotechnical
Reliability, P. Thoft-Christiansen, Ed, 1982.

[2] Bjerrum, L. "Embankments on soft ground," Proc., ASCE
Specialty Conference on Earth and Earth Supported
Structures, v.2:   111-159.

[3] D'Appolonia, D.J., E. D'Appolonia, and R.F. Brissette,
"Settlement of spread footings on sand," Proc. ASCE, v.
94(SM5), 1968.

[4] Hilldale (-Cunningham), C., "A probabilistic approach to
estimating differential settlement of footings on sand,"
Thesis submitted to the Massachusetts Institute of
Technology in partial fulfillment of the requirements for
the degree Master of Science in Civil Engineering, 1971.

[5] Ladd, C.C. and R. Foott, "A new design procedure for
stability of soft clays," Proc. ASCE, v. 100(GT7), pp.
763-786, 1974.

[6] Spikula, D., "Statistical estimation of soil engineering
properties, an application," Thesis presented to the
Massachusetts Institute of Technology in partial fulfillment
of the requirements for the degree Master of Science in
Civil Engineering, 1982.

APPENDIX: Vector to vector propogation of variance:

If $\underline{y} = \underline{g}(\underline{z})$ is a vector of predicted variables, then

$$E[\underline{y}] \simeq g(E[\underline{z}])   ,$$

$$\underline{C}_y \simeq \underline{G}\,\underline{C}_z\,\underline{G}^t   ,$$

where $\underline{C}_z$ is the covariance matrix of $\underline{z}$, and $\underline{C}_y$ the
covariance matrix of y. $\underline{G}$ is the matrix of derivatives of
$\underline{g}(\underline{z})$ having ij^{th} element $\partial g_i(\underline{z})/\partial z_j$.

PROBABILISTIC NATURE OF SOIL PROPERTIES

Raymond N. Yong* M.ASCE

ABSTRACT

The causes or reasons for observed variations in measured soil properties of apparent identical samples can be attributed to at least four primary factors: (a) source material, (b) methods of soil sampling, (c) types and procedures used for soil testing, and (d) selection of models used for data analysis. The integrity of a soil material is defined not only by its compositional components, but also by the constituent natural bonds and the resultant interactions between the various constituents and components. Variations in the four primary factors, in combination with the uncertainties arising in proper characterization of soil integrity result in the production of physical soil property values which cannot be easily accepted as "true" soil properties. The influence of the factors in relation to compositional and structural aspects of soil material can be seen in the differences in reported soil property values. Quality of samples and the degree to which they are representative of the soil mass investigated are identified as primary controls on soil property variability.

Introduction

Much has been said about the variability and differences in reported values of soil properties for apparently "identical" soil samples. By and large, the major thrust of analyses on the above has focussed on the general thesis that the random nature of soil properties can indeed be attributed to four primary factors: (a) source material, (b) methods of soil sampling, (c) types and procedures of soil testing, and (d) selection of models used for data analyses.

The causes or reasons for observed variation in measured soil properties in "identical" samples can be traced to the influences exercised by the following factors:

(a) the basic soil material and means whereby its integrity as a soil mass is established,
(b) soil sampling tools and procedures,
(c) choice and implementation of laboratory test techniques,

---

* William Scott Professor of Civil Engineering and Applied Mechanics and Director, Geotechnical Research Centre, McGill University, Montreal, Canada.

(d) selection and use of models for data analysis.

Since the essential elements of a soil "property" lie in the basic structure of soil (including all the attendant interactions and bondings), attention in the evaluation of "real" soil properties should be directed towards a better appreciation of soil material as an assemblage consisting of stable soil structural units. Viewing the probability of occurrence of a particular soil proprety value as a measure of the uncertainty about the likelihood of such a property being a real property, actually present or measured, it is necessary to define more clearly the problem in terms of "what gives rise to a specific soil property". In doing so, the probabilistic nature of soil properties itself becomes more evident.

The Stable Soil Structural Unit

The three principal components generally recognized as basic participants in the development of a soil material assemblage are: (a) solids consisting of mineral and non-mineral particles, (b) fluid - with dissolved and non-dissolved electrolytes, and (c) air. Whilst the composition of the third component, air, can most easily be assumed to be "standard" and therefore "constant" without any serious loss in accuracy in representation of the system, the same cannot be said for the composition of the other two components. Because of the highly variable nature of:

(1) proportions of the various constituents in the components and the components themselves,
(2) arrangement of the individual and collective groups of particles forming the stable soil structural units, and
(3) types and distribution of bonds formed in the soil material assemblage.

the immediate points of consideration in the evaluation of soil proper- ties are to ensure that the nature, distribution of the basic soil structural units (i.e. micro-structure) and basic interactions between the units are properly factored into the analysis.

The actual composition of a natural soil element consisting of an assemblage of particles and contained fluid and air, at any one time, is a function of several processes that combine to produce that parti- cular composition at that particular time. The particular attributes arising therefrom are specific to the geologic material involved and the spontaneous reactions - generally in the direction of a decrease in the free energy of the system. At any specified time, the integrity of the soil material, (i.e. the state of the material which is respon- sible for the soil properties), can be considered in terms of (a) the constituent natural bonds, and (b) the results of interactions between the various constituents and components. The fundamental unit within the system can be identified as the stable soil structural unit. Not only will the characteristics and properties of each dissimilar structural unit be different, the interactions and bondings between the units which combine to form the total soil structure will also

differ. The formational characteristics of each soil structural unit
and the interactions depend on specific local environmental constraints
developed in regard to the balance of internal energy. The probability
of occurrence P_i of a structural unit possessing a particular property
is a direct function of its energy state E_i. Whilst several structural
units may individually possess the same energy state, the converse does
not necessarily hold, i.e. there is only one energy state uniquely
identified with the particular configuration of any one stable soil
structural unit. In a heterogeneous medium such as a soil material
assemblage, consisting of an infinite number and variety of stable
structural units, the overall (macroscopic) soil property measured is
the result of the averaging of the local properties. In that regard,
homogeneity or the lack thereof constitute significant factors that
will influence production of "representative" soil properties.

     In granular soils, the basic structural units are single grains.
Their role in the development of granular soil mechanical properties
such as compressibility and strength, depend on: (a) mineralogy,
(b) size distribution and proportions of the various basic units
comprising the granular soils, (c) mode of packing, interlocking and
cementation (i.e. fabric), (d) surface texture and morphology. For
the same granular soil type, since particle interaction is through
the basic soil structural units, packing, i.e. fabric, is by far the
single most important factor that needs to be reproduced identically
if variability effects in measurement of mechanical properties - due
to granular soil sampling - are to be eliminated.

     In cohesive soils, the basic structural unit can be single
particles (or units), tactoids, flocs and peds. These in turn can form
basic aggregate groups of various sizes and shapes through various
types and methods of bonding. Figures 1a,b and 2 show two typical
clay soil fabrics which demonstrate the preceding points. The formation of the various kinds of basic structural units can be traced to
the processes of soil formation - including thereby soil compositional
features and bond mechanisms. Since fabric and total soil structure
combine all the various basic structural units, it is important to
reproduce all these items exactly if variability effects in cohesive
soil sampling are to be eliminated.

     Figure 3 shows a general flow scheme beginning with soil source
and ending with the reporting of soil property measurements. In between
the many sources of variations and "errors" that can occur because of
choices made, routes followed, and procedures adopted, render the
problem of selection of a typical representative soil property indeed
difficult. To further illustrate the problem, the type of strength
test indicated in Fig. 3 for example, can be discussed solely in terms
of type of test - e.g. triaxial $[\sigma_2 = \sigma_3,\ \sigma_1 \neq \sigma_2 \neq \sigma_3]$, plane strain, torsional, hollow cylinder, direct and simple shear, etc. In doing so,
the type of equipment used, the Length/Diameter ratios of specimens,
and all the other items shown in Fig. 3 must be fully considered in
regard to the physical control on the production of a measured strength
property. Obviously, simple differences in any individual item -
between tests and test samples - will produce differing results even

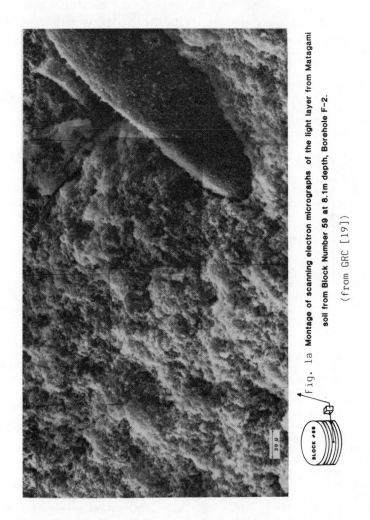

Fig. 1a **Montage of scanning electron micrographs of the light layer from Matagami soil from Block Number 59 at 8.1m depth, Borehole F-2.**

(from GRC [19])

Fig. 1b Montage of scanning electron micrographs of the dark layer from Matagami soil from Block Number 59 at 8.1m depth, Borehole F-2.

(from GRC [19])

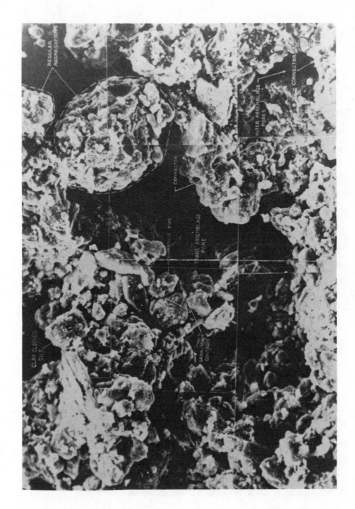

Fig. 2   Overall Microfabric: Tucson Silty Clay - U.S.A. - Fresh Water Alluvial
Deposit (from Collins and McGown [11])

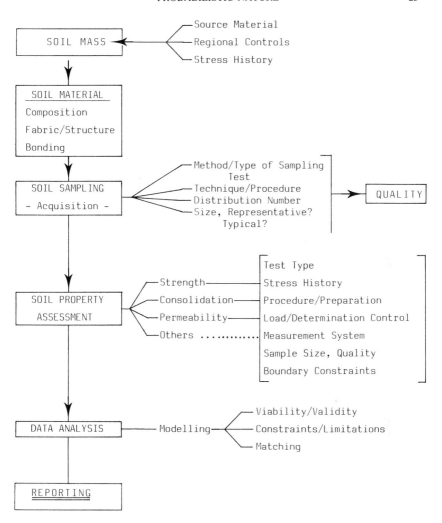

Fig. 3 General Schematic Showing the Many Sources
of Variabilities in Final Reporting of
Soil Properties

if "identical" samples are tested. The tables given in the Appendix
give some examples of the wide variety of test results obtained in
soil property testing. They are meant to highlight the problem and to
alert the engineer to the probabilistic nature of soil properties

Structural Units, Structure and Sampling

Considering that source material and regional controls are
indeed responsible for the spatial variations of total soil structure,
it is noted that to develop the basis for analysis, distinction must be
made between block sampling and borehole sampling as indicated in Fig.
3. The smaller samples obtained from a block sample provide a cluster
of values of a measured property which corresponds to the physical
location of the block within the subsoil. In turn, the block can be
represented by coordinates in respect to a global coordinate system.
Block sampling provides the capability for evaluation of the mean and
inherent scatter of the property at a particular point in the subsoil.
In contrast to the preceding, borehole sampling furnishes single values
of the measured property at various points in a borehole - i.e. borehole sampling provides one with the means for establishing the spatial
trend of the measured property.

The significance of the inputs provided by source material and
regional controls as shown in Fig. 3, on the production of variability
in soil composition profile can be well demonstrated by Fig. 4. The
two samples shown in the Figure represent core samples taken from a
site located about 150 km south of James Bay within the Lake Ojibway
plain - in Quebec, Canada. The varves of light grey, very soft clay
and hard-to-stiff silty/silty clay (approximately 3/4 cm thick) are
derived from two separate source sediments: (a) a north-easterly
source of crystalline Precambrian rocks in New Quebec, and (b) a
north-westerly source derived in part from sedimentary Palaezoic rocks
of the Hudson Bay lowland [19].   The darker varves represent the
winter layers whilst the lighter varves show the summer layers. The
typical composite profile for the region reported in the study [38]
from the results of [21] is shown in Fig. 5. The presence of significantly varying amounts of carbonate has been noted to be higher in
the summer silt than in the overlying winter clay layer for the proximal varves [19,38]. A typical distribution for carbonate content is
shown in Fig. 6, with the corresponding soil-water potential given in
Fig. 7. Since the soil-water potential is a good indicator of the
energy state of the soil material, it is clear from Fig. 7 that the
high degree of variability of the energy profile will reflect directly
on the physical properties and performance of the material.

Whilst it might be argued that the example shown in Figs. 4
through 7 might be an extreme case - because of the varved nature of
the clay deposit, the example nevertheless serves to demonstrate the
significance of the illustrative flow scheme shown in Fig. 3, i.e.

(a) Geologic and Regional input and controls
(b) Requirements for sampling - type, procedure and size
    of samples,

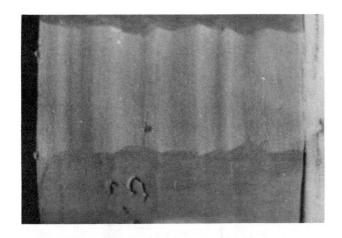

Pre-Cochrane
Distal Varves
Block 59, 8.0 m

Cochrane I
Proximal Varves
Block 39, 6.0 m

Fig. 4 Varves in Two Core Samples (GRC [19])

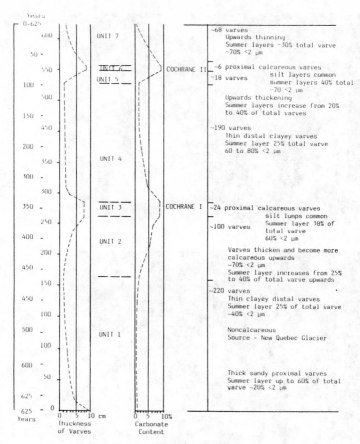

Fig. 5 Nature of the Varved Clay Section at Matagami
Total Mean Thickness ~12 m
(from Hardy [21])

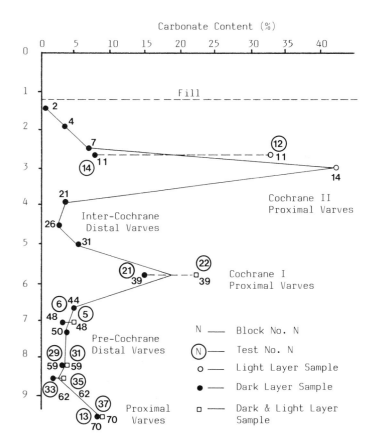

Fig. 6 Profile of Carbonate Content vs. Depth for Samples
Used in Suction Tests

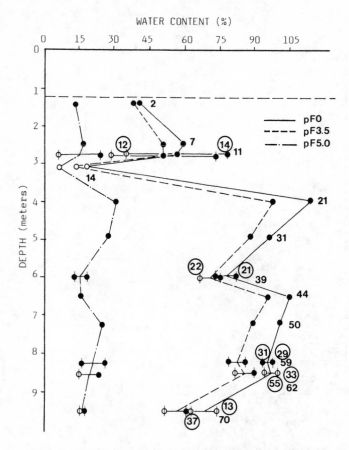

Fig. 7   Profile of Soil Water Potential in Terms of Water
         Content vs. Depth for Matagami Clays

(c) Testing requirements.

Obviously, the selection of test varve sample is very significant. Which varve? How many varves? Can one perform a proper test
on one varve?

In regard to soil sampling, it is relevant to note that sample
disturbance effects are almost inevitably encountered in the acquisi-
tion of samples - either in terms of release of in-situ stresses and/or
expansion of soil sample. In soft clays changes in total stresses
inevitably associated with sample removal from the ground [24,37,45,49,
50] will initiate a process of softening. Because of the low permeability of clays, final stress equilibrium under reduced effective
stresses will be re-established after some considerable period of time.
In consequence, the effective stress parameters c' and ϕ' are seen to
be influenced indirectly by sampling effects but more directly by the
undrained strength which depends on the equilibrium status of the
material at the time of testing.

In the case of sampling of stiff fissured clays, lateral expansion (due to load release) may cause some opening of fissures, resulting thereby in increasing mass permeability. Possible resultant
softening of soil samples initiated from the open fissures under zero
effective stress [55] will cause a reduction in strength. With time
and continued load transfer internal stress equilibrium will be
achieved. The final formation of stable soil structural units and the
resultant bond re-establishment and interactions between structural
units will produce an overall stable structural configuration similar
to a normally consolidated clay. If the softened clay is not sheared,
though ϕ' will remain constant, c' will tend to reduce to a minimum or
even a zero value. However, when the softened clay is sheared past
its peak value, ϕ' will also decrease and discrepancies in strength
parameters will be further observed.

Resultant soil softening can occur locally in overconsolidated
clays also as a result of internal migration of pore water [49] into
the shear zone from less highly strained regions in the clay. It is
noted that in boulder clays, melt water can remove fines thereby
creating permeable passages between sand and gravel pockets. Fabric
modifications can occur by desiccation, infiltration and organic
action. Whilst various macrofabric features are apparent, the features
of particular geotechnical interest include the effect of cracks and
joints [32]. The sediments are often complex [51].

In tills, because of the presence of larger fragments of
coarse material, it is often necessary to discard or ignore the larger
stones and boulders in the sampling process. The assumption made is
that the properties of the till are more likely to be controlled by
their matrices, which tend to be less sensitive to disturbance and are
free from structural discontinuities.

In sensitive clays, the arrangement of particles (fabric) and
the presence of bonds at interparticle contacts [39,52] constitute
significant factors in the development of soil strength. In the

sensitive clays of Eastern Canada for example, observed deviations from Mohr-Coulomb failure criterion performance for soils tested at low pressures in standard triaxial testing procedures, reflect the bonded nature and inherent anisotropy of the soil [12,34,35,41]. A comparison between the stress-strain behaviour of the soils at low and high confining pressures suggests that the difference in constitutive performance may be due to the fact that bonds are progressively destroyed by the application of high consolidation pressures [58]. The development of intrinsic stresses and bonds between soil particles depends to a large extent on the geologically applied effective stresses. The computed cohesion intercept in a Mohr-Coulomb type analysis is a function of the test procedure rather than a real property of the material itself [14].

Alluvial deposits are often stratified and contain both sand and silt layers. Samples may be readily pulled apart at the boundaries of basic lumps ('peds') in the sampling process because of the planes of weakness which apparently exist between the peds [45]. Alluvial materials exhibit high permeabilities at low effective stresses, leading thereby to varying degrees of softening during drilling [43,45].

Soil Testing

The determination of soil properties from laboratory tests for evaluation of soil performance relative to specific situations, using soil specimens obtained from different locations in the field implicitly assumes that the samples obtained are representative of the respective in-situ (Fig.3) conditions. In this regard the validity of investigations carried out in the laboratory rests not only on the type of tests performed in the laboratory, but also on the quality of the samples obtained and to the extent to which they are representative of the stratum from which they are taken [13]. Relative to shear strength evaluation [48] discrepancies between field and laboratory strength were attributed to (a) sampling, (b) sample orientation, (c) sample size, (d) rate of shearing, (e) softening, and (f) progressive failure. Extensive information and reports regarding the suitability of different test techniques have been documented earlier (e.g. 1,2,3). From the many sources of variations noted in Fig. 3, we note that the importance of standardization of test techniques lies not only in the need to establish "common" procedures and utilization of standard equipment, but also in the requirement to establish mutual understanding between various test laboratories and researchers insofar as communication and comparison of test results are concerned. Variability in test measurements can be minimized with "common" procedures and techniques.

In addition to variations in test procedures, a large contributor to differing soil property test results is the integrity or quality of the test sample (Fig. 3). Common causes of sample disturbance: (a) change of stress conditions due to unloading, (b) change of structure due to mechanical effects, (c) change of water content or void ratio, and (d) change of composition due to chemical effects, have been discussed by several researchers (e.g. 22, 36, 42).

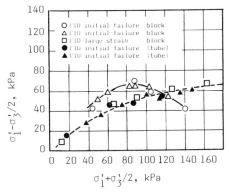

Fig. 8 Effective Stress Envelopes of a Champlain
Clay from Saint-Louis Yamaska (after
LaRochelle and Lefebvre [**41**])

Shear Strength

As a demonstration of variabilities in soil strength for apparently similar soil samples, the shear strength of London clay [10]
showed changes in the undrained strength ratio (parallel to bedding/
normal to bedding) from 0.88 to 0.86 for 38 mm x 76 mm and 101.6 mm x
203.2 mm specimens respectively. Skempton and Hutchinson [48] also
found a wide scatter amongst the undrained triaxial shear strength
for specimens of various sizes. The relative strength varied from 1.9
to 0.66 for specimens measuring 2.5 cm x 2.5 cm to 30 cm x 60 cm,
respectively. This was attributed principally to the likely presence
of fissures in the test specimens. In another study Marsland and
Butler [31] observed c' and ϕ' varying from 11.0 kN/m^2 to 7.18 kN/m^2
and 24^0 to 23.5^0 corresponding to specimens of sizes 38 mm x 76 mm to
76 mm x 152.4 mm or 127 mm x 254 mm.

The influence of sample quality, as controlled by the type of
sample used to procure soil samples, on the experimentally determined
soil property has been demonstrated [42]. Different unconfined compressive strengths for some Eastern Canadian sensitive clays corresponding
to specimens obtained from sampling tubes of sizes 54 mm, 75 mm and
100 mm were obtained as shown in Table 1. The quality of a specimen
was evaluated through the determination of tangent moduli Eu. In
general test samples obtained from reshaped 54 mm tubes yielded "better"
results than the 54 mm standard tubes with inside clearances. While
strength improved by 20% or more, the moduli increased by 50-100%. In
comparison to 54 mm tubes, the test values obtained from test samples
derived from 75 mm and 100 mm tubes showed improvements in strength
by as much as 100%, and in modulii by 150%. The conclusion that one
reaches is that lower strengths are obtained because of "disturbance"
effects in sampling - using smaller tubes. Strength variability can
be traced to the quality of the sample used. LaRochelle and Lefebvre
[41] also investigated effective strength envelopes as effected by
block samples and tube samples and shown in Fig. 8. It can be seen
that when the clay is "destructured" by consolidation effects, the

Site	Type of Tube	c_{u_f}/c_{u_v}	E_u (kPa)
Saint-Vallier (7.9 mm)	54 mm standard	0.32	1800
	54 mm reshaped	0.66	3500
	75 mm reshaped	0.81	4100
	100 mm reshaped	0.80	5200
Saint-Vallier (14.0 m)	54 mm standard	0.75	4100
	54 mm reshaped	0.90	7600
	75 mm reshaped	0.88	5900
	100 mm reshaped	0.84	9000
Yamaska (6.1 m)	54 mm standard	1.02	5500
	54 mm reshaped	1.24	8300
	75 mm reshaped	1.11	7200
	100 mm reshaped	1.57	9000

TABLE 1 Comparative Results of Quality Tests (from LaRochelle et al. [42])

peak strengths measured on the tube samples were reduced to values comparable to large strain strengths obtained on block samples. The maximum difference in peak strengths between the block and tube samples is 30%.

The changes or variations in soil strength due to mechanical disturbances resulting from the intrusion of samplers into various types of soils have been well documented: e.g. (a) sensitive soils, [17,25,40]; (b) stiff clays [36]; (c) sensitive slightly over consolidated clays [33]; and (d) London clay [50,57].

Raymond et al. [40] observed that the deviator stress and coefficient A at failure varied for samples obtained from different types of samplers, as shown in Table 2 and Fig. 9. Morgenstern and Thomson [36] evaluated the compressive strength (uu) of soil specimens obtained through block sampling, Shelby tube and Pitcher samplers and observed that for certain corresponding water contents, compressive strengths increased by 207 kN/m^2 for tube samples in comparison to block samples. Milovic [33] noted that in relation to sensitive clay, effective stress parameters c' and ∅' varied from 17 kN/m^2 to 12.75 kN/m^2, and from 18.3° to 17.2° respectively in comparing samples obtained from blocks and Shelby samplers. In the case of unconfined compressive strengths block samples exhibited strengths of around 0.6 kg/cm^2 whilst Shelby samples and Piston samples showed strengths of about two-thirds and one-third less respectively than those obtained with block samples.

The relationship between water content, effective mean normal stress and undrained strength for different specimen types relative to glacial lake deposits are shown in Fig. 10 [5]. It can be seen that different test samples obtained through slurry (Ko consolidated, and isotropically consolidated), block samples and tube samples exhibit

$\sigma_1 - \sigma_3$	Consolidation pressure 200 kN/m² (4000 lb/ft²)					
$(\sigma_1 - \sigma_3)_f$	Block	Osterberg	Swedish	Sharp	Piston	Open
1/4	0.579	0.761	0.547	0.569	0.884	0.683
1/2	0.551	0.641	0.578	0.533	0.742	0.600
3/4	0.561	0.652	0.573	0.551	0.695	0.572
7/8	0.576	0.671	0.554	0.553	0.677	0.557
15/16	0.582	0.701	0.550	0.559	0.685	0.547
1	0.607	0.728	0.547	0.573	0.674	0.535

Table 2   Pore Pressure Coefficient A for all Samples from 3 m Depth
(from Raymond et al. [40]).

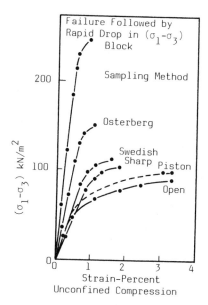

Fig. 9   Typical Unconfined Compression Test Results (from
Rayment et al [40])

different relationships. The consolidation and shear behaviour of the
undisturbed block specimen at the overburden stress level is that of
a preconsolidated material, changing at higher stress levels to that of
a normally consolidated material. The undrained shear behaviour of
undisturbed block specimens and remoulded slurry specimens at high Ko
stresses are similar, indicating thereby that structural effects from

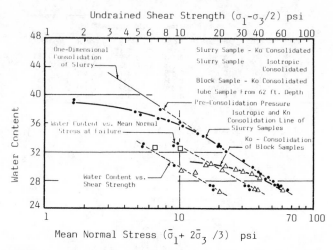

Fig. 10   Relationship Between Water Content, Effective Mean Normal
Stress and Undrained Strength for Lambton Clay (after
Adams and Radhkrishna [5]).

remoulding are probably not predominant. The undrained strength of
specimens at the Ko and at the equivalent isotropic stress condition
(no loss in suction) were identical for both undisturbed block specimens and slurried specimens. Specimens allowed to take on water
(suction loss) showed a significant loss in strength. This corresponds
to the change (reduction) in the internal energy state of the material.
The importance of fabric, soil structure and geology in regard to
choice of sampling location, quality and size of specimens for element
and model tests shown in Tables 3 and 4 cannot be overemphasized [45].
A scheme which relates the sampling procedure with quality class for
evaluation of soil properties and specimen sizes in support of Fig. 3
can be produced to assist in the selection of both quality samples
and "representative" soil property values.

Consolidation Characteristics

Figure 11 shows void-ratio-log effective stress curves for
different size specimens whilst variations of coefficient of consolidation with specimen size are plotted in Figs. 12 and 13. Figure 11
shows that different e-log p' relationships are obtained when different
size specimens are tested in the oedometer. The void ratio decrement
is lesser as the diameter of the test sample is increased. Figures
12 and 13 indicate that larger-sized samples exhibit higher values of
coefficient of consolidation. Remoulded samples show lesser values
of C_v as compared to undisturbed samples. This is consistent with the
thesis that soil structural strength becomes measurably reduced
because of the disruption of in-situ bonds which typify the natural

Quality class	Properties	Purpose	Typical sampling procedure
1	Remoulded properties Fabric Water content Density and porosity Compressibility Effective strength parameters Total strength parameters Permeability* Coefficient of consolidation*	Laboratory data on in situ soils	Piston thin walled sampler with water balance
2	Remoulded properties Fabric Water content Density and porosity Compressibility* Effective strength parameters* Total strength parameters*	Laboratory data on in situ insensitive soils	Pressed or driven thin or thick walled sampler with water balance
3	Remoulded properties Fabric A* 100% recovery. Continuous B* 90% recovery. Consecutive	Fabric examination and laboratory data on remoulded soils	Pressed or driven thin or thick walled samplers. Water balance in highly permeable soils
4	Remoulded properties	Laboratory data on remoulded soils. Sequence of strata	Bulk and jar samples
5	None	Approximate sequence of strata only	Washings

* Items changed from German classification.

Table 3 Quality Classes (from Rowe [45])

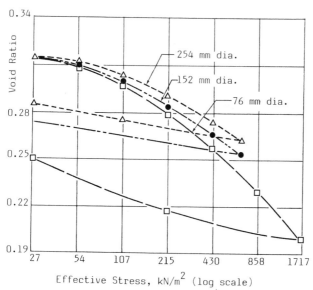

Fig. 11 Void Ratio-Log Effective Stress Curves for Different Size Specimens from Grassyards Road, Kilmarnock (after McGown and Radwan [32])

Minimum sizes of specimens from Quality 1 thin walled piston samples of natural clay deposits.
Foundations for buildings, bridges, dams, fills.   Stability of natural slopes, cuts open or retained.
Exceptions: deposit too $\left\{\begin{matrix}\text{weak} & \text{variable}\\ \text{strong} & \text{stoney}\end{matrix}\right\}$

Clay type	Macro fabric	Mass, k, m/s	Parameter	Specimen size, mm*
Non-fissured Sensitivity < 5	None	10^{-10}	c_u, $c'\phi'$ / m_v, c_v	37 / 76
	Pedal, silt, sand layers, inclusions. Organic veins	$10^{-9}-10^{-6}$	c_u / $c'\phi'$ / m_v / c_v	100–250 / 37 / 75 / 250
	Sand layers > 2 mm at < 0·2 m space	$10^{-6}-10^{-5}$	$c'\phi'$ / m_v	37 / 75
Sensitivity > 5	Cemented with any above		c_u, $c'\phi'$, m_v, c_v	50–250‡
Fissured†	Plain fissures	10^{-10}	c_u / $c'\phi'$ / m_v, c_v	250 / 100 / 75
	Silt or sand filled fissures	$10^{-9}-10^{-6}$	c_u c_v / $c'\phi'$ / m_v	250 / 100 / 75
Jointed	Open joints		ϕ'	100
Pre-existing slip			$c_r\phi_r$	150 or remoulded

* 75 mm samples for continuous Quality 2–4 samples for fabric examination, strength as index test, c_u and $c\phi$ for intact low sensitivity.
† Size and orientation dependent on fissure geometry.
‡ Tube area ratio 4%, sample dia. 260 mm.

Table 4   Specimen Sizes (from Rowe [45])

soil. Remoulded soil integrity is seen to depend primarily on the stability of the stable structural units and the interactions developed thereby. The results shown in Figs. 14 and 15 indicate also that the direction of flow (drainage) has a significant influence on the value of C_v obtained. A comparison of other consolidation parameters - m_v, p_c, C_v obtained from testing of samples derived from different samplers is shown in Tables 5 and 6. It can be seen that samples derived from soil sampling blocks generally exhibit systematically higher values of p_c and lower values of m_v in comparison to other sampler specimens.

Atterberg Limits

Since Atterberg limits are generally determined from testing of remoulded soil samples, variations in test results obtained occur through marked differences in apparently similar soil samples, method of interpretation used to evaluate the "limit" value, and through quality of sample.

An example of variations of Atterberg limits in a soil profile where three different soil sampler types have been used to obtain test samples are shown in Fig. 16. As noted in the figure,

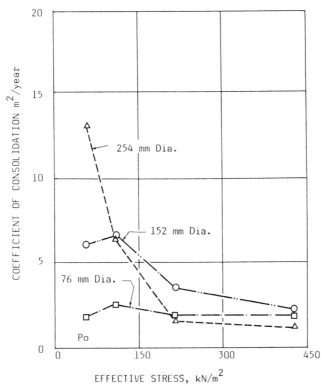

Fig. 12 Variation of the Coefficient of Consolidation With Applied
         Effective Stress for Different Size Specimens from Craufurd-
         land, Kilmarnock (after McGown and Radwan [32]).

the variations in liquid limit are considerably larger than those
shown for plastic limit values.

Composition

        To further demonstrate the influence and importance of a proper
knowledge of soil composition effects, consider the X-ray diffractograms for a natural bonded sensitive clay from St. Louis, Quebec
shown in Figs. 17a and 17b. The clay is characterized by horizontal
laminae of different tones, light gray bands 5-10 mm thick alternating
with dark gray bands of approximately the same thickness. It can be
seen that laminae contain the same types of minerals. Non-clay
minerals identified include an abundance of plagioclase feldspar,
quartz and possibly of lesser quantities of hornblende.

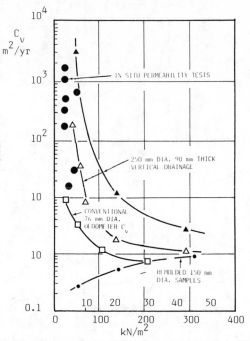

Fig. 13 Large Diameter Sample Consolidation Test Data
(after Rowe [45])

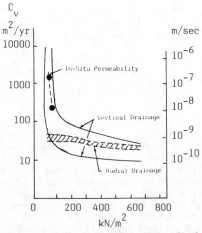

Fig. 14 Consolidation Rate Test Data, Moira Marl (after
Rowe [45])

Soil	P (kN/m^2)	$\Delta P/P$	c_v (m^2/yr) (1) from Δu	(2) from Δv	Ratio (2)/(1)
Mexico City Clay	19.3	2.0	4.08	3.99*[2]	0.97
Undisturbed	107.5*[1]	3.0	0.29	0.46*[2]	1.57
*A	513.0*[1]	0.15	2.8	0.04*[2]	0.014
Brown London Clay	191.7	0.8	0.99	0.67*[3]	0.68
with silt inclusions	344.7	0.6	0.98	0.52*[3]	0.53
Undisturbed *B	551.6	0.6	0.92	0.41*[3]	0.45
Blue London Clay	175.8	1.15	0.31	0.30*[3]	0.98
Undisturbed *2	380.6	0.096	0.35	0.22*[3]	0.62
	413.6	0.33	0.27	0.21*[3]	0.78
M6 Boulder Clay	0		1.35	1.77*[3]	1.31
	41.3	0.67	2.75	3.13*[3]	1.14
FM Remoulded *C	82.7	0.33	3.92	3.51*[3]	0.89

*A 113 mm dia. oedometer

*B 101.6 mm dia. x 101.6 mm high dissipation test

*C 101.6 mm dia. x 101.6 mm high dissipation test

*1 Above the preconsolidation load

*2 Using Casagrande's log time method

*3 Fitting at 50% primary volume change.

Table 5   Values of c_v in the Laboratory Determined from Dissipation of Pore Pressure and from Rate of Volume Change (from Bishop and Al-Dhahir [9]).

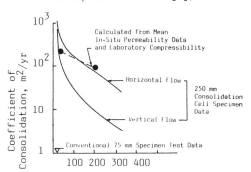

Fig. 15   Consolidation Rate Data on London Clay, Ardleigh (after Rowe [45])

Site	Type of Specimen	No. of Tests	Pressure, σ_1, kg/cm²	Coefficient of Volume Change, m_v cm²/kg	Preconsolidation Pressure p_c kg/cm²
St. Simon, Quebec, Canada	Block	6	0.08 to 0.16 0.16 to 0.24 0.24 to 0.36	0.0202 0.0280 0.0448	0.90
	Piston	5	0.08 to 0.16 0.16 to 0.24 0.24 to 0.36	0.0212 0.0315 0.0473	0.80
	Shelby	5	0.08 to 0.16 0.16 to 0.24 0.24 to 0.36	0.0516 0.0598	0.60
Nicolet, Quebec, Canada	Block	5	0.08 to 0.16 0.16 to 0.24 0.24 to 0.36	0.0251 0.0382 0.0520	0.65
	Piston	4	0.08 to 0.16 0.16 to 0.24 0.24 to 0.36	0.0325 0.0416	0.60
	Shelby	4	0.08 to 0.16 0.16 to 0.24 0.24 to 0.36	0.0752 0.1273 0.2860	0.45

Table 6 Consolidation Test Results (from Milovic [33])

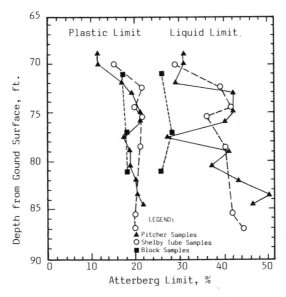

Fig. 16 Moisture Contents and Atterberg Limits with Depth
(after Morgenstern and Thomson [36])

Similarly in regard to X-ray diffractograms (Fig. 18) of the
Matagami varved clay shown previously in Figs. 4 through 7, consisting of winter dark layers and summer light layers of varying thick-
nesses (0.4 cm - 5 cm) we note from Table 7 that within the same
varve, clay contents may differ by more than 30%, and specific
surface areas may vary more than 80 m^2/gm. It is observed from Fig.
18 that whilst minerals present in dark layers and light layers within the same block are almost the same, non-clay minerals - carbonate
contents vary appreciably as shown previously in Fig. 6. Variations
in activity, liquidity indices and charge density are also apparent
in the Table. Differences in Ip corresponding to dark and light
layers may be of the order of 30% and more and charge densities may
change by 5 coloumb/cm^2 x 10^{-5}.

The data shown in Figs. 19 and Table 8 with respect to tests
on samples for Blocks No. 6 and No. 7, obtained from the same depth
at Outardes 2, Quebec, indicate that the two blocks have different
particle size distribution, different proportions of clay minerals
and different water contents and Atterberg limits. A further analysis of Block No. 6 as per the scheme shown in Fig. 20 points to the
fact that when comparing the permeability results of samples 1I with
1II, 2I and 2II, and 3I and 3II (Table 9), the permeability value
differs for each set of samples. This suggests that the difference
in permeability for samples treated identically in each class, is

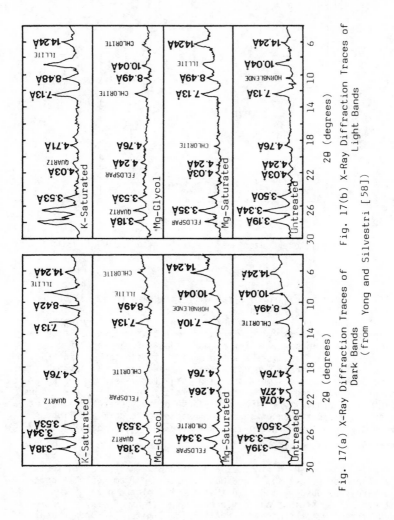

Fig. 17(a) X-Ray Diffraction Traces of   Fig. 17(b) X-Ray Diffraction Traces of
          Dark Bands   Light Bands
          (From Yong and Silvestri [58])

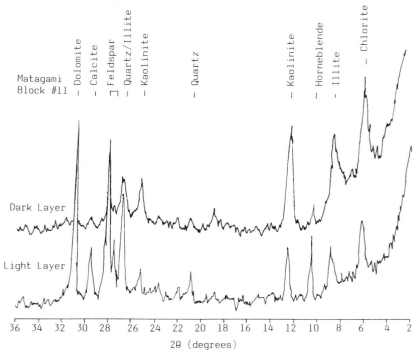

Fig. 18   X-Ray Diffraction Traces of Dark and Light Layer in a Block
of Matagami Clay

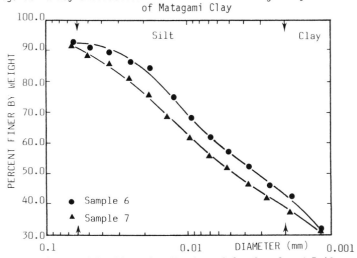

Fig. 19   Particle-Size Distribution of Samples 6 and 7 (from
Yong et al. [59])

BLOCK NO.	DEPTH	VARVE THICKNESS (m)	VARVE DESCRIPTION	CARBONATE (%)	WATER CONTENT			Ip	$\frac{w_n-w_p}{w_x-w_p}$ Li	<2 μm (%)	ACTIVITY $\frac{Ac}{Ip}$ (%<2 μm)	SPECIFIC SURFACE (S.S.) (m²/g)	ACTIVITY $\frac{Ac(ss)}{Ip}$ S.S.	CHARGE DENSITY Coul.cm⁻² ×10⁻⁵ $\frac{(CEC \times 9.65)}{S.S.}$
					w_n	w_x	w_p							
9	1.9	Laminated	Laminated	4.6	34.7	57.1	24.0	33.1	0.3	52	0.64	113.7	0.29	3.56
11 D	2.8	5+	Cochrane II Thick	7.95	72.6	82.4	28.8	53.6	0.8	93	0.58	138.9	0.39	4.22
11 L			Proximal Varves	21.75	33.0	37.7	19.5	18.2	0.7	60	0.30	57.7	0.32	9.37
17 D	3.5	4.7	"	7.2	86.7	68.7	26.5	42.2	1.4	79	0.53	115.4	0.37	4.43
17 L			"	9.7	65.1	55.5	25.7	29.8	1.3	68	0.44	84.1	0.35	6.65
22 D	4.0	<1.2	Inter-Cochrane Variable	0.22	113.0	92.5	32.6	59.9	1.3	75	0.80	73.6	0.81	3.75
22 L			Distal Varves	1.1	108.0	86.0	33.1	52.9	1.4	67	0.79	70.0	0.76	4.33
27 D	4.6	0.8	"	0.94	91.5	74.3	29.4	44.9	1.4	72	0.62	81.8	0.55	4.30
27 L			"	0.63	91.6	73.6	30.7	42.9	1.4	76	0.56	80.6	0.53	3.45
34 D	5.4	2.7	Cochrane 1 Thick	4.5	104.3	73.3	30.2	43.1	1.7	70	0.62	97.1	0.44	4.56
34 L			Proximal Varves	11.5	63.3	45.5	24.9	20.6	1.9	62	0.33	54.9	0.38	8.80
39 D	6.0	3.6	"	9.6	86.6	61.5	26.0	35.5	1.7	84	0.42	109.9	0.32	4.09
39 L			"	17.6	72.0	56.8	24.7	32.1	1.5	68	0.47	99.0	0.32	4.63
41 D	6.1	3.1	"	9.0	90.5	80.0	27.6	52.4	1.2	84	0.62	144.4	0.36	3.44
41 L			"	9.4	86.8	73.0	27.9	45.1	1.3	82	0.55	134.0	0.34	3.57
45 D	6.6	1.7	Pre-Cochrane Thin	2.6	99.8	77.9	30.5	47.4	1.5	88	0.54	106.2	0.45	3.41
45 L			Distal Varves	3.7	97.9	74.5	29.8	44.7	1.5	N.A.	N.A.	95.7	0.47	4.67
59 D	8.0	1.4	"	1.7	95.9	83.7	30.8	52.9	1.2	90	0.59	105.6	0.50	2.45
59 L			"	2.2	85.7	65.0	27.7	37.4	1.6	69	0.54	84.3	0.44	3.37
70 D	9.5	3.1	Pre-Cochrane Intermed.	2.2	87.7	82.6	29.8	52.8	1.1	72	0.73	105.5	0.50	3.64
70 L			Proximal Varves	7.3	55.6	41.0	26.0	15.0	2.0	62	0.24	47.9	0.31	9.33

D = Dark Layer   L = Light Layer

TABLE 7   Index Test Results (from GRC [19])

| Block no. | Depth (m) | Water content (%) | Atterberg limits | | | Liquidity index I_L | Shear strength (Swedish cone) | | Sensitivity |
			W_L	W_P	I_P		undisturbed (kg/cm^2)	remoulded (kg/cm^2)	
3	2.55—2.85	40.0	38.5	16.9	21.6	1.97	0.819	0.037	22
5	2.40—2.70	50.5	34.5	18.0	16.5	1.97	0.753	0.037	20
		37.0	34.5	18.0	16.5	1.14	0.583	0.0174	33
1	2.40—2.70	33.8	32.3	20.2	12.1	1.15	—	—	—
2	2.40—2.70	40.36	31.8	19.6	12.2	1.70	—	—	—
6	2.70—3.0	47.0	45.4	17.3	28.1	1.06	1.0	0.037	27
7	2.70—3.0	41.0	44.2	17.6	26.6	0.88	0.87	0.067	13
bulk sample (remoulded)	2.25—3.30	41.3	37.4	17.7	19.7	1.2	—	0.22*	

*Laboratory vane test.

Table 8   Index Properties of the Outardes 2 Clay (from Yong et al. [59])

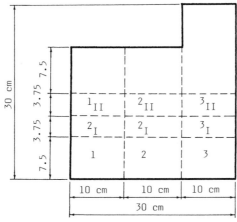

Fig. 20   Block Sampling (from Becker [7])

due to the differences in composition. This is further reflected in Table 10, which shows the mineralogical composition of the block, and Table 11 which summarizes the index properties of the soil.

CONCLUDING REMARKS

It is apparent that quality and the degree to which samples are representative of the soil stratum under investigation are by far the most important factors that control the derivation or determination of "real" soil property. For a particular project under study, there is a definite need for the engineer to identify predictions which are not only critical to the safety of the project, but must also satisfy functional and economic requirements. As noted [26]

Leaching Solution Used	K' cm/sec. from Leaching Tests $P = 17.5$ kPa	K' cm/sec from Consolidation Tests $P = 17.5$ kPa
B.L.*	–	4×10^{-8}
Buffer pH = 4.0		
1_I	3.2×10^{-7}	6×10^{-8}
1_{II}	4.2×10^{-7}	6.8×10^{-8}
Treated with pH = 10.5		
2_I	2.77×10^{-7}	8.27×10^{-8}
2_{II}	2.7×10^{-7}	2.1×10^{-7}
Distilled Water		
3_I	2.24×10^{-7}	3.0×10^{-8}
3_{II}	2.07×10^{-7}	3.35×10^{-7}

* B.L. = before leaching, i.e. unleached sample.

Table 9   Permeability Values of Samples from Consolidation and Leaching Tests (from Becker [7])

Depth (cm) in the Block Sample #6	Mineral	Percent (natural)	Amorphous Material	Percent
11.5-19.0	Quartz	42.76	SiO_2	3.6
	Feldspar:		Fe_2O_3	3.45
	Albite	13.64	Al_2O_3	0.97
	Microline	13.34	Total	8.02
	Illite	3.1		
	Hornblende	6.4		
	Dolomite	3.1		
	Total	82.34		
0.0-7.5	Quartz	8	SiO_2	7.8
	Feldspar	3	Fe_2O_3	4.0
	Illite	5	Al_2O_3	7.1
			Total	18.9
	Hornblende	2		
	Chlorite + Kaolinite	3		
	Total	21		

Table 10   Mineralogical Composition and Amorphous Content (from Becker [7])

Depth (cm) in the Block #6	Water Content W %	Atterberg Limit		Shear Strength (Swedish Cone)		Sensitivity	Spec. Gravity G_S
		W_L %	W_P %	Undisturbed Kpa	Remoulded Kpa		
11.5-19.0	33	33	21.5	131.4	15.39	8.5	2.85
0.0-7.5	47	45.4	17.3	98.00	3.63	27.0	----

Table 11   Index Properties of the Soil (from Becker [7])

the reliability of predictions and the consequences of predictions are inherent items needed for consideration in the selection and execution of appropriate actions.

Because of inherent variations in soil composition and consistency during formation, and particularly because of the effect of regional controls, soil properties need to be regarded as random variables. As noted by Lumb [29] it is not unlikely that variabilities of soil will sometimes overshadow test imperfections. Acknowledging the spatial variability of soil properties, Lumb [30] estimated that a minimum number of samples would be of the order of 10^4 for a full three dimensional analysis. To study variability over one dimension either laterally or vertically, approximately 20 to 100 samples from a single population might be considered satisfactory to reflect the internal variability. The use of "probability-of-failure" approach rather than the traditional "factor-of-safety" method of analysis accounts not only for the uncertainties present in soil resistance [6] but also for those evidenced in the applied loads and the analytical modelling of soil and soil-structural behaviour.

Models of stochastic and Markov processes [4, 30,56] are conceptually good but generally difficult to apply in situations where data points are few, irregularly spaced and are derived from different sources [53,54]. The use of techniques involving trend functions chosen to suit the complexity of the situation and the number of data points available can combine data from different field and laboratory tests on separate or block samples, and are especially suitable in cases where data points are few and irregularly spaced. By distinguishing between biased and unbiased data points, together with calibration of data sets when more than one testing technique is involved, the basic parameters describing the property can be derived [53]. The autocorrelation functions can be established to allow for examination of anisotropy of the property.

The use of the concept of stable soil structural units permits one to examine the fundamental elements in the soil which exhibit control on the demonstrated soil property. Whilst much work remains to be done to fully establish the mathematical framework which adequately describes the physics of interaction of these stable units, it is nevertheless useful to evaluate basic soil performance and properties in terms of "how these stable units perform".

Acknowledgement

The assistance provided by Dr. M.L. Sadana in the preparation of this paper is fully acknowledged. This study was supported by the Natural Sciences and Engineering Research Council [NSERC] of Canada, Grant No. A-882.

References

1. ASTM Special Technical Publication No. 361, "Laboratory Shear
    Testing of Soils", Ottawa, American Society for Testing and
    Materials, Philadelphia, 1963

2. ASTM Special Technical Publication No. 483, "Sampling of Soil and
    Rock", American Society for Testing and Materials, Philadelphia,
    1971

3. ASTM Special Technical Publication No. 740, "Laboratory Shear
    Strength of Soil", Chicago, American Society for Testing and
    Materials, Philadelphia (eds. R.N. Yong and F.C. Townsend),
    1981

4. Alonso, E.E. (1976) "Risk Analysis of Slopes and Its Application
    to Slopes in Canadian Sensitive Clays", Geotechnique, 26,
    No. 3, 453-472

5. Adams, J.I. and Radhakrishna, H.S. (1971) "Loss of Strength Due to
    Sampling in a Glacial Lake Deposit", ASTM STP 483, American
    Society for Testing and Materials, Philadelphia, 109-120

6. Athanasiou-Grivas, D. and Harr, M.E.(1979) "A Reliability Approach
    to the Design of Soil Slopes, Design Parameters in Geotechnical
    Engineering, Proc. of the 7th European Conf. on S.M.F.E.,
    British Geotechnical Society, Vol. I, 95-99

7. Becker, R. (1979) "The Influence of Leaching Amorphous Material on
    the Mechanical Properties of a Sensitive Clay", Thesis submitted
    in partial fulfillment of the requirements for the degree of
    Master of Engineering, Dept. of Civil Engineering and Applied
    Mechanics, McGill University

8. Bell, J.M. and Arrigoni, E.L. (1970) "Shape Influence on Triaxial
    Strengths", Proc. of the 8th Annual Symposium on Engineering
    Geology and Soil Engineering, Idaho, 237-254

9. Bishop, A.W. and Al-Dhahir, Z.A. (1970) "Some Comparison Between
    Laboratory Tests, In-Situ Tests and Full Scale Performance
    with Special Reference to Permeability and Coefficient of
    Consolidation", Proc. of the Conf. on 'In-Situ Investigations
    in Soils and Rocks', British Geotechnical Society, 251-276

10. Bishop, A.W. , and Little, A.L. (1967) "The Influence of Size and
    Orientation of the Sample on the Apparent Strength of the
    London Clay at Maldon, Essex", Proc. Geotechnical Conf. (Oslo)
    1, 89-96

11. Collins, K. and McGown, A. (1974) "The Form and Function of Micro-
    fabric Features in a Variety of Natural Soils", Geotechnique,
    24, No. 2, 223-254

12. Conlon, R.J. and Isaacs, R.M.F. (1971) "Effect of Sampling and
    Testing Techniques on the Shear Strength of a Glacial-Lacustrine

Clay from Welland, Ontario", ASTM STP 483, American Society for Testing and Materials, Philadelphia, 3-10.

13. Cooling, L.F. (1962) "Field Measurements in Soil Mechanics", Geotechnique 12, 77-104

14. Crawford, C.B. (1963) "Cohesion in an Undisturbed Sensitive Clay", Geotechnique 13, 132-146

15. Dernevich, V.P. and Massarsch, K.R. (1979) "Sample Disturbance and Stress-Strain Behaviour", Geotechnical Eng. Div., Proc. ASCE, Vol. 105, GT9, 1001-1016

16. Duncan, J.M. and Seed, H.B. (1966) "Strength Variation Along Failure Surfaces in Clay", Journal of Soil Mech. and Found. Div., Proc. ASCE, SM6, 81-104

17. Eden, W.J. (1971) "Sample Trial in Overconsolidated Sensitive Clay" In Sampling of Soil and Rock, ASTM STP 483, American Society for Testing and Materials, Philadelphia, 132-142

18. Edan, W.J. and Law, K.T. (1980) "Comparison of Undrained Shear Strength Results Obtained by Different Test Methods in Soft Clays", Canadian Geotechnical Journal, 17, 369-381

19. Geotechnical Research Centre (1982) "Geotechnical Utilization of Natural Soil Materials of the James Bay Area in View of Frost Heaving and Long Term Leaching Effects", F.C.A.C. Programme Majeur, Progress Report No. 1.

20. Green, G.E. and Reades, D.W. (1975) "Boundary Conditions Anisotropy and Sample Shape Effects on the Stress-Strain Behaviour of Sand in Triaxial Compression and Plain Strain", Geotechnique, 25, No. 2, 333-356

21. Hardy, L. (1976) "Contributions a l'etude geomorpholoqique de la portion Quebecoise des basses terres de la Baie de James", Ph.D. Thesis, Dept. of Geography, McGill University, 264 p, plus maps and photos

22. Hvorslev, M.J. (1948) "Subsurface Exploration and Sampling of Soils for Civil Engineering Purposes", U.S. Waterways Experiment Station, Vicksburg, Miss.

23. Ladd, C.C. (1967) in Proceedings of the Geotechnical Conference, Oslo, Vol. 2, 112-115 (Discussion)

24. Ladd, C.C. and Lambe, T.W. (1964) "The Strength of Undisturbed Clay Determined from Undrained Tests", Proc. Symp. Laboratory Shear Testing of Soils (Ottawa), ASTM Special Technical Publication 361, American Society for Testing and Materials, Philadelphia, 342-71

25. Lafleur, J. (1970) "Influence of Mechanical Disturbance of Consolidation Characteristics of Clays", M.Sc. Thesis, Department de
Genie Civil, Universite Laval, Quebec, P.Q.

26. Lambe, T.W. (1973) "Predictions in Soil Engineering", Geotechnique,
23, No. 2, 149-202

27. Lambe, T.W. (1973) "Laboratory and Field Testing of Soils for
Their Strength, Deformation and Rheological Properties",
Proc. of the 8th Int. Conf. on SM. and F.E., Mockba, U.S.S.R.
Session on Up-to-date methods of investigating the strength
and deformability of soils, Vol. 3, 3-25

28. Loh, A.K. and Holt, R.T. (1974) "Directional Variation in Undrained
Shear Strength and Fabric of Winnipeg Upper Brown Clay",
Canadian Geotechnical Journal, 11, 3, 430-437

29. Lumb, P. (1971) "Precision and Accuracy of Soil Test", Proc. 1st
Int. Conf. Applications of Statistics and Probability in Soil
and Structural Engineering, Hong Kong Univ. Press, Hong Kong,
329-346

30. Lumb, P. (1975) "Spatial Variability of Soil Properties", Proc.
2nd Int. Conf. Applications of Statistics and Probability in
Soil and Structural Engineering, Hong Kong Univ. Press, Hong
Kong, Vol. 2, 397-422, F.R. Germany, published by Deutsche
Gesellschaft fur.

31. Marsland, A. and Butler, M.E. (1967) "Strength Measurements on
Stiff Fissured Barton Clay from Fawley, Hampshire", Proc.
Geotechnical Conf., Oslo, 1, 139-46

32. McGown, A. and Radwan, A.M. (1975) "The Presence and Influence of
Fissures in the Boulder Clays of West Central Scotland",
Canadian Geotechnical Jour., 12, 84-97

33. Milovic, D.M. (1971) "Effect of Sampling on Some Soil Characteris-
tices", ASTM STP 483, American Society for Testing and
Materials, Philadelphia, 164-179

34. Mitchell, R.J. (1970) "On the Yielding and Mechanical Strength
of Leda Clays", Canadian Geotechnical Journal, 7, 297-312

35. Mitchell, R.J. (1972) "Some Deviations from Isotropy in a
Lightly Overconsolidated Clay", Geotechnique, 22, 459-467

36. Morgenstern, M.R. and Thomson, S. (1971) "Comparative Observations
on the Use of the Pitcher Sampler in Stiff Clay", ASTM STP 483,
American Society for Testing and Materials, Philadelphia, 180-
191

37. Noorany, I., and Seed, B. (1965) "In-Situ Strength Characteristics
of Soft Clays", Proc. American Society of Civil Engineers,
Vol. 91, March, 49-80

38. Quigley, R.M., Sethi, A.J., Boonsinsuk, P., Sheeran, D.E. and Yong, R.N. (1982) "Geological Control on Soil Composition and Properties, Lake Ojibway Clay Plain, Matagami, Quebec", 35th Canadian Geotechnical Conf., Montreal, Quebec, Sept. 461-479

39. Quigley, R.M. and Thompson, C.D. (1966) "The Fabric of Anisotropically Consolidated Sensitive Marine Clay", Canadian Geotechnical Journal, 3, 61-73

40. Raymond, G.P., Townsend, D.L. and Lojkacek, M.J. (1971) "The Effect of Sampling on the Undrained Soil Properties of the Leda Clay", Canadian Geotechnical Journal, 8, 4, 546-557

41. LaRochelle, P. and Lefebvre, G. (1971) "Sampling Disturbance in Champlain Clays", ASTM STP 483, American Society for Testing and Materials, Philadelphia, 143-163

42. LaRochelle, P., Sarraith, J., Tavenas, F.,Roy, M. and Leroueil, S. (1981) "Causes of Sampling Disturbance and Design of a New Sampler for Sensitive Soils", Canadian Geotechnical Journal, Vol. 18, No. 1, 52-66

43. Rowe, P.W. (1968) "Failure of Foundations and Slopes in Layered Deposits in Relation to Site Investigation Practice", Proc. Institution of Civil Engineers, Suppl. 1, 73-131

44. Rowe, P.W. (1971) "Representative Sampling in Location, Quality and Size", Sampling of Soil and Rock, ASTM STP 483, American Society for Testing and Materials, Philadelphia, 77-108

45. Rowe, P.W. (1972) "The Relevance of Soil Fabric to Site Investigation Practice", Geotechnique 22, No. 2, 195-300

46. Sangrey, D.A. (1972) "Naturally Cemented Sensitive Soils", Geotechnique 22, No. 1, 139-152

47. Sarrailh, J. (1975) "Contribution a l'etude des methodes d'echantill onnage des argiles sensibles", M.Sc. Thesis, Dept. de Genie Civil, Universite Laval, Quebec, P.Q.

48. Skempton, A.W. and Hutchinson, J. (1969) "Stability of Natural Slopes and Embankment Foundations", State of the Art 7th Int. Conf. SM and F.E., State of the Art Vol., 291-334

49. Skempton, A.W. and LaRochelle, P. (1965) "The Bradwell Slip, a Short Term Failure in London Clay", Geotechnique, 15, 221-42

50. Skempton, A.W. and Sowa, V.A. (1963) "The Behaviour of Saturated Clays During Sampling and Testing", Geotechnique 13, 269-290

51. Soderman, L.G. and Kim, Y.D. (1970) "Effect of Groundwater Levels on the Stress History of the St. Clair Clay Till Deposit", Canadian Geotechnical Journal, Vol. 7, No. 2, 173-187

52. Soderman, L.G. and Quigley, R.M. (1965) "Geotechnical Properties of Three Ontario Clays", Canadian Geotechnical Journal, 2, 167-189

53. Tabba, M.M. and Yong, R.N. (1981) "Mapping and Predicting Soil Properties Theory", Journal of the Engineering Mechanics Div., ASCE, Vol. 107, No. EM5, 773-793

54. Tabba, M.M. and Yong, R.N. (1981) "Mapping and Predicting Soil Properties: Applications", Journal of the Engineering Mechanics Div., ASCE, Vol. 107, No. EM5, 795-811

55. Terzaghi, K., (1936) "Relation Between Soil Mechanics and Foundation Engineering", Proc. Presidential address to First Inter. Conf. on Soil Mechanics and Foundation Engineering, Cambridge, Mass., Vol. 3, 13-18

56. Van Marcke, E.H. (1977) "Probabilistic Modeling of Soil Profiles", Journal of the Geotechnical Engineering Div., ASCE, Vol. 103, No. GT 11, 1227-1246

57. Ward, W.H., Samuels, S.G., and Butler, M.E. (1959) "Further Studies of the Properties of London Clay", Geotechnique, Vol. 9, 33-58

58. Yong, R.N. and Silvestri, V. (1979) "Anisotropic Behaviour of a Sensitive Clay", Canadian Geotechnical Journal, Vol. 16, No. 2, 335-50

59. Yong, R.N., Sethi, A.J., Booy, E. and Dascal,   (1979) "Basic Characterization and Effect of Some Chemicals on a Clay from Outardes 2", Engineering Geology, 14, 83-107

60. Yong, R.N. and Tabba, M.M. (1981) "On the Random Aspects of Shear Strength", Laboratory Shear Strength of Soil, ASTM, STP 740, R.N. Yong and F.C. Townsend eds., American Society for Testing and Materials, 485-501

APPENDIX 1

From LaRochelle et al. (42)   SHEAR STRENGTH DATA

[A]

Site	Type of Test	Cu_f/Cu_v	E_u (kPa)	Percent Variation Cu_f/Cu_v	E_u
Saint-Vallier (7.9 m)	54mm standard	0.32	1800	0% base **	0% base **
	54mm reshaped*	0.66	3500	106	94
	75mm reshaped	0.81	4100	153	128
	100mm reshaped	0.80	5200	150	189

Saint-Vallier clay is a sensitive clay from Quebec, Canada

E_u = Young's modulus; Cu_f = unconfined compressive strength; Cu_v = field vane strength

* reshaped sampler is the sampler without internal clearance and having tapered length equal to 1/4 (inside diameter)
** base value used to determine percent variation for other values

[B]

Site	Source	Unconfined Compression (UC) Cu_f (kPa)	ε_f (%)	Unconsolidated Undrained (UU)** Cu_f (kPa)	ε_f (%)	Percent Variation UC Cu_f	ε_f	UU Cu_f	ε_f
Saint-Louis	Block	65	1.06	61.5	1.07	0% base	0% base	0% base	0% base
	200 mm tube	60	1.03	62.75	1.02	-8*	-3*	-2*	-5*

*(-) variation indicates that the reported values are smaller than the base values
** unconsolidated undrained strength refers to quick triaxial tests performed on 38 mm diameter samples cut from block and tube samples

unconfined compression data refers to 9 tests on block samples and 7 tests on tube samples

unconsolidated undrained compression data refers to 11 tests on block samples and 6 tests on tube samples.

From Bishop and Little (10)

Site	Clay	Size of Specimen	Ch/Cn	% Variation
Maldon	brown London clay	38mm x 76 mm 101.6 mm x 203.2 mm	0.88 0.86	0% base -2

Ch = undrained strength in compression specimens with their axis parallel to bedding.

Cn = undrained strength in compression specimens with their axis normal to bedding.

From Rowe (44)

[A] Soil	Condition	Undrained Shear Strength* (kN/m^2) at Depths (m)				% Variation			
		2m	3m	4m	5m	2m	3m	4m	5m
Organic Alluvial Clay (London)	Dryhole driven 100 mm tube	17.5	40	15	20		0% Base		
	Water filled hole driven 100 mm tube	13	NA	23	22.5	-25	NA	53	13
	Water filled hole pushed thin walled 100 mm tube	20	32	23	26	14	-20	53	30
	Water filled hole thin walled piston sampler 260 mm dia.	22.5	17.5	16	16	29	-56	7	-20

* undrained shear strength refers to triaxial undrained shear strength data taken from the depth profile

NA = not available.

[B]	Soil	Sample Size and Rate of Strain	Undrained Strength (kN/m²) 5m Depth	% Variation
	Kimmeridge Clay (London Clay)	38 mm dia., .05%/min	63	0% base
		38 mm dia. x 50 mm, .03%/min	70	11
		38 mm dia., .0025~.004%/min	52	-17
		100 mm dia., .004%/min	40	-37
		Pocket Penetrometer	110	75

[C]	Soil	Source	Undrained Shear Strength* (kN/m²)		% Variation	
			5m	6.5 m	5 m	6.5 m
	London Clay	Dry borehole driven	67	44	0% base	0% base
		Water filled borehole driven	68	70	1.5	59
		Minimum strength based on 100 mm sampling	58	63	-13	43
		Water filled borehole 254 mm** piston sampler	60	38	-10	-14

* undrained shear strength refers to triaxial undrained shear strength data taken from the depth profile

** volume of sample tested = 150 x volume of (38 mm x 76 mm) sample.

From Yong and Tabba (60)

[A]	Site	Sample	Unconfined Compression Strength* (kPa)	% Variation
	St. Jean Vianney	Block	290	0% base
			330	14
			480	66
			555	91

St. Jean Vianney clay is a sensitive clay from Quebec, Canada

* unconfined compressive strength was determined from strain controlled unconfined compression tests on 38 mm x 76 mm samples cut from the same block.

[B]	Soil	Sample	Consolidated Undrained Triaxial Strength* (kPa)	% Variation
	St. Jean Vianney	Block Sample	335	0% base
			350	4
			412	23
			420	25
			427	27
			452	35
			470	40

* consolidated undrained triaxial strength was determined on the undisturbed block specimens from a sensitive clay from St. Jean Vianney, Quebec, corresponding to a confining pressure of 137.8 kPa and a strain rate of 0.1143 mm/min.

From Ladd (23)

Location	Soil	Depth, m	Ratio of Undrained Strength UC or UU / Field Vane	UC or UU Triaxial CU[a]	Type of Sample	% Variation Field Vane	Triaxial
Gulf of Mexico	soft clay	0 to 6	0.54	0.85	Shelby	0% base	
M.I.T. Campus	N.C. Boston blue clay	29	0.55	0.34[b]	76mm Piston	2	-60
Mexico City	Mexico City clay	--	0.64	0.74	--	19	-13
Kawasaki Japan	N.C. clays	20 to 45	0.67	0.58	76mm Shelby	24	-31
Lagunillas Venezuela	N.C. clay	6	0.81	0.82	71.1 mm Shelby	50	-3
Skabo, Norway	N.C. clay (st = 5)	10 to 16	1.04	0.88	NGI[c]	93	4

Location	Soil	Depth, m	Ratio of Undrained Strength UC or UU		Type of Sample	% Variation	
			Field Vane	Triaxial CU[a]		Field Vane	Triaxial
Maglerund Norway	quick clay (St>100)		1.4	0.82	NGI	159	-3
Ottawa, Canada	leda clay	6.5 to 10	1.91	0.98	block	253	15
		17	~1.0	~0.95	piston	~85	~12

a for confining pressure = overburden pressure

b Ko - consolidation tor triaxial CU

c NGI = Norwegian Geotechnical Institute

UC = unconfined compression

UU = unconsolidated undrained

From Loh and Holt (28)

Soil	Inclination Angle θ*	Unconfined Compression Strength (kN/m²)	% Variation
Lacustrine Clay	0°	51.7	50
	15°	42.71	24
	30°	42.76	24
	45°	34.47	0% base
	60°	49.64	44
	82°	97.90	184
	90°	126.86	268

* θ is the angle of inclination between the natural bedding plane and the sample base

- lacustrine clay is from Winnipeg, Manitoba

- unconfined compression strength was determined on specimens having dimensions of 35.6 mm in diameter and 76.2 mm in height.

From Duncan and Seed (16)

Soil	Sample	% of Initial Water Content	c'_{ac} in kg per sq.cm	c'_{ic} in kg per sq.cm	% of Consolidation Water Content	$(\sigma_a-\sigma_l)_f$ in kg per sq.cm	$\bar{A}_f$	ε_{af} in %	Time to Failure hr	c'_{if} in kg per sq.cm	σ'_{8f} in kg per sq.cm	% variation $\bar{A}_f$
Silty Marine Clay	VPS-3	87.5	3.67	1.81	52.9	2.70	1.07	3.1	5.25	3.61	0.91	18
	VPS-4	85.3	0.64	0.35	77.4	0.51	0.91	4.0	5.75	0.66	0.15	0% base
	VPS-5	87.3	1.39	0.70	64.3	1.03	1.15	3.2	6.0	1.34	0.31	26
	VPS-6	89.5	2.14	1.07	59.1	1.58	1.14	4.2	7.0	2.07	0.49	25
	VPS-8	87.7	2.90	1.44	53.7	2.12	1.18	3.6	6.75	2.77	0.65	30
	VPS-9	91.0	3.72	1.77	51.8	2.76	1.07	3.5	4.5	3.66	0.90	18
	HPS-4	93.1	0.69	1.61	65.2	0.81	0.75	11.1	4.50	1.12	0.31	15
	HPS-5	85.8	1.20	3.15	52.1	1.65	0.70	9.6	4.50	2.28	0.63	8
	HPS-6	90.1	0.34	0.81	74.8	0.41	0.69	9.0	5.0	0.61	0.20	6
	HPS-7	89.3	0.99	2.40	57.5	1.28	0.72	10.0	5.25	1.72	0.44	11
	HPS-9	88.8	1.47	3.98	51.1	2.23	0.67	10.6	5.25	3.04	0.81	3
	HPS-11	92.3	1.66	4.00	52.8	2.24	0.68	10.6	4.50	3.04	0.80	5
	HPS-12	85.5	1.52	3.18	52.5	1.77	0.65	9.8	5.25	2.43	0.66	0% base

Silty marine clay is from San Francisco Bay Mud

VPS refers to vertical plane strain test

HPS refers to horizontal plane strain test

$\bar{A}_f$ refers to pore pressure parameter

$(\sigma_a-\sigma_l)_f$ refers to deviator stress at failure

From Conlon and Isaacs (12)

Site	Sample	Depth m	Shear Strength* Inclination Angle		% Variation	
			$0°$ (kN/m^2)	$45°$	$0°$	$45°$
Welland	Block	22.34	48.83	15.8~38.3	0% base	-68~-22
	127 mm samples	23.01	40.69	33.51	-17	-31
	76 mm samples	22.61	38.78	NA	-21	-

Welland clay is a sensitive lacustrine clay of medium to high plasticity from Welland, Ontario

127 mm samples were obtained through 127 mm outside diameter fixed rod piston sampler
76 mm samples were obtained either through 73 mm outside diameter thin-walled Shelby tubes or fixed-rod piston samplers of similar diameter

* shear strength was determined through unconsolidated undrained triaxial tests on specimens of 38 mm diameter and 76 mm length corresponding to a cell pressure of 207 N/m².

shear strength data as reported is taken from the general data.

From Eden and Law (18)

[A]

Site	Inclination Angle i (deg)	Natural Water Content (%)	Failure Strain (%)	A_f	Peak Strength (kPa)	Strength Ratio	% Variation in Strength Ratio
South Gloucester	0	70.3	1.9	0.45	22.8	1.00	28
	30	71.6	1.9	0.58	22.5	0.99	27
	45	67.3	1.8	0.68	19.3	0.85	9
	60	72.3	1.6	0.71	17.7	0.78	0% base
	90	70.3	2.2	0.77	18.3	0.80	3

South Gloucester clay is a Leda clay from Ottawa, Canada

Peak strength refers to peak shear strength determined through triaxial compression tests on specimens cut from various angles i, from block samples.

[B]

Site	Test Type	Natural Water Content (%)	Failure Strain (%)	A_f	Peak Strength (kPa)	% Variation in Peak Strength
South Glouster	compression	64.9	1.8	0.38	26.1	74
	compression	65.3	2.1	0.43	27.5	83
	extension	65.3	1.0	1.10	15.5	3
	extension	65.4	1.3	1.00	15.0	0% base

[C] Site	Test Type	Natural Moisture Content (%)	Failure Strain (%)	Peak Strength (kPa)	% Variation in Peak Strength
South Gloucester	Controlled stress path plane	67.8	4.5	29.0	23
	Strain test on horizontal specimen				
	Undrained triaxial	70.6	4.7	28.0	19
	Compression test on vertical specimen	70.2	1.41	23.5	0% base
		69.2	1.51	24.6	9

From Morgenstern and Thomson (36)

Soil	Sample Type	Compression Strength kN/m²	% Variation
Till	Block	413.68	0% base
	Shelby	655.0	58
	Pitcher	655.0	58

Compressive strength was determined from unconsolidated undrained triaxial tests on specimens measuring 38 mm in diameter and 76 mm in height.

Compression strength values are taken corresponding to a water content of 15% from the general data

Till was obtained from the City of Edmonton, Canada.

From Rowe (45)

Soil	Sample	Undrained Shear Strength (kN/m²) Water Content (%)		% Variation in Water Content (%)	
		15	20	15	20
Wadhurst clay	38 mm* sample	140	75	211	67
	250 mm** sample	75	45	67	0% base

* 38 mm diameter samples were tested using lubricated platens at a strain rate of 0.03%/min.

** 250 mm diameter samples were tested using lubricated platens at a strain rate of 0.01%/min.

Wadhurst clay is stiff blue/grey fissured clay.

Undrained shear strength corresponds to undrained triaxial strength.

From Drnevich and Massarsch (15)

Soil	Shear Strain (%)	Shear Stress (kPa)		% Variation	
		Undisturbed Sample	Disturbed Sample	Undisturbed Sample	Disturbed Sample
Clayey silty sand	0.25	27	22	23	0% base
	0.50	35	27	59	23
	0.75	39	33	77	50

Clayey silty sand had 11% clay, 31% silt, 49% sand, and 8% gravel. Density - 1.87 t/m^3, water content - 32%, 28% liquid limit, 24% plastic limit and plasticity index - 14.

Shear stress corresponds to torsional shear test

Undisturbed sample means remoulded sample which was loosely compacted and then isotropically consolidated.

Disturbed sample corresponds to the one which already experienced maximum shear stress in the first test and was allowed to reconsolidate for about 24 hours.

Torsional Shear Test was performed with undrained conditions and the rate of loading (stress controlled) was about 0.033% shear strain per minute.

From Raymond et al. (40)

Soil	Sample Type	Unconfined Compression Strength (kN/m^2)	% Variation
Leda clay	Open tube	90	0% base
	Piston sampler	97	8
	Sharp tube	102	13
	Swedish sampler	112	24
	Osterberg sampler	150	67
	Block sample	250	178

Leda clay is a sensitive clay from Ontario, Canada.

Sharp tube, open tube and piston sampler are Shelby tube sampler types.

Swedish sampler refers to Swedish Standard Piston sampler.

Osterberg sampler refers to Osterberg hydaulic sampler with a fixed piston.

From Milovic (33)

Soil	Sample	Unconfined Compression Strength (kg/cm^2)
St. Simon Clay	Block	0.6
	Piston	0.41
	Shelby	0.22

St. Simon clay is a sensitive slightly overconsolidated clay from Quebec, Canada

Unconfined compression tests were performed at a rate of strain of approximately 0.22%/minute.

From Sangrey (46)

Clay	Varve Orientation (deg)	Shear Strength (kg/cm^2)	% Variation
Matagami Mines Clay	0°	1.1	0% base
	20°	0.85	22
	40°	0.7	36
	45°	0.65	41
	60°	0.75	32

Matagami Mines clay is a sensitive varved clay from Quebec, Canada.

Shear strength was determined through drained, strain-controlled triaxial tests on specimens cut at different angles.

Varve orientation is the angle of varves to the horizontal.

Shear strength values are taken from the general relationship.

SHEAR STRENGTH PARAMETERS c - ∅

From Raymond et al. (40)

Soil	Sample Type	c' (kN/m²)	∅' (deg.)	% Variation c'	% Variation ∅'
Leda clay	Block(a) below p_c* value	110	0	0% base	-22
	(b) above p_c value	0	22	-110	0% base
	Osterberg(a) below p_c value	50	0	-55	-22
	(b) above p_c value	0	26	-110	-18

Leda clay is a sensitive clay from Ontario, Canada

Shear strength parameters c', ∅' were determined through consolidated undrained triaxial tests on specimens of 50 mm diameter and 100 mm height using standard Geonor equipment

*p_c = preconsolidation pressure

From Marsland nad Butler (31)

Soil	Sample Size	c' (kN/m²)	∅' (deg)	% Variation c'	% Variation ∅'
Boston clay	38 mm × 76 mm	11.01	24	0% base	0% base
	76 mm × 152 mm	7.18	23.5	-35	2
	61 cm square shear box	8.14	27	-26	13

Boston clay is a stiff fissured clay.

c' and ∅' correspond to 38 mm × 76 mm and 76 mm × 152 mm samples which were obtained from triaxial tests

61cm square shear box is an in-situ test with a horizontal plane

From Milovic (33)

[A] Site	Type of Specimen	c' (kg/cm²)	ø' (deg)	% Variation c'	% Variation ø'
St. Simon	Block	0.173	18.3	0% base	0% base
	Piston	0.157	17.5	-9	4
	Shelby	0.130	17.2	-25	6
Nicolet	Block	0.135	18.0	0% base	0% base
	Piston	0.125	16.8	7	7
	Shelby	0.095	16.0	30	11

From Green and Reades (20)

Soil	Initial Porosity (%)	Triaxial $ø_T$ (deg)	Plane Strain $ø_P$ (deg)	% Variation $ø_T$	% Variation $ø_P$
Sand	40	38	42.5	0% base	12
	42	36.7	40.3	-3	6
	44	35.1	38.1	-8	0
	46	33.75	36	-11	5

$ø_T$ and $ø_P$ values are taken from the general relationship

Triaxial data was obtained by triaxial compression tests on rectangular samples

Plane strain data corresponds to drained vertical plane strain tests.

From Skempton and Hutchison (48)

Soil	Approx. Inclination of failure planes to horizontal	Tests			Peak Strength Parameters		% Variation	
		Type	Size	Orientation	c' (kN/m²)	φ' (deg)	c'	φ'
Wraysburg clay	± 0°	shear box	6 cm	horiz.	34.47	19.2	4	1
		triaxial	38 mm	inclined	33.03	19.0	0% base	0% base
	± 55°	triaxial	38 mm	vertical	35.42	22.3	7	17
	± 35°	triaxial	38 mm	horiz.	32.07	22.5	3	18

Wraysbury clay is a blue London clay.

From Bell and Arrigoni (8)

Soil	Tests	Friction Angle* Porosity (%)				% Variation for different porosities			
		33% (deg)	35% (deg)	37% (deg)	39% (deg)	33%	35%	37%	39%
Quartz sand	cylindrical free ends	36.8	35.6	33.5	31	0% base	-3	-9	-16
	cubical free ends	34.6	33.1	31.5	30	-6	-10	-14	-18
	conventional triaxial	39.8	37.5	35.2	32.7	8	2	4	11
	direct shear	38.4	36.2	33.8	31.5	4	-2	8	-14

* friction angle values are taken corresponding to different porosities from the general relationships obtained.

From Lambe (27)

Clay	Condition	Sandy Clay $\bar{c}$(tsm)	$\tilde{\varnothing}$	Fat Clay $\bar{c}$(tsm)	$\tilde{\varnothing}$	F.S.	% Variation in F.S.
Cliff side soil	Peak	2.3	37	1.6	20	2.02	0% base
	Residual	0	33	0	0	0.50	-75
	Remoulded	0	33	0	22	1.03	-49

Cliff side soil was from Amuay, Venezuela.

CONSOLIDATION CHARACTERISTICS

From Milovic (33)

Site	Type of Specimen	No. of Tests	Pressure, σ, kg/cm^2	Coefficient of Volume Change, m_v, cm^2/kg	Preconsolidation Pressure, p_c kg/cm^2	% Variation in p_c
St. Simon	Block	6	0.08 – 0.16	0.0202	0.90	0% base
			0.16 – 0.24	0.0280		
			0.24 – 0.36	0.0448		
	Piston	5	0.08 – 0.16	0.0212	0.80	-11
			0.16 – 0.24	0.0315		
			0.24 – 0.36	0.0473		
	Shelby	5	0.08 – 0.16	0.0516	0.60	-33
			0.16 – 0.24	0.0598		
			0.24 – 0.36	0.0738		

From Milovic (33) Cont'd

Site	Type of Specimen	No. of Tests	Pressure, σ, (kg/cm²)	Coefficient of Volume Change, m_v, (cm²/kg)	Preconsolidation Pressure, P_c (kg/cm²)	% Variation in P_c
Nicolet	Block	5	0.08 – 0.16 0.16 – 0.24 0.24 – 0.36	0.0251 0.0382 0.0520	0.65	0% base
	Piston	4	0.08 – 0.16 0.16 – 0.24 0.24 – 0.36	0.0325 0.0416 0.0541	0.60	-8
	Shelby	4	0.08 – 0.16 0.16 – 0.24 0.24 – 0.36	0.0752 0.1273 0.2860	0.45	-30

Both St. Simon clay and Nicolet clay are sensitive slightly overconsolidated clays from Quebec, Canada

From Morgenstern and Thomson (36)

Soil	Depth m	Sample Type	Preconsolidation Pressure, P_c (kN/m²)	Coefficient of Compressibility a_v (m²/kN × 10⁻⁵)	Coefficient of Consolidation c_v (m²/yr)	% Variation		
						P_c	a_v	c_v
Till	23.5	Block Shelby Pitcher	268.13 128.70 471.90	6.9 6.0 5.5	3.43 0.55 1.06	0% base -52 76	0% base -13 -20	0% base -83 -69
	24.7	Block Shelby Pitcher	193.05 257.40 514.80	6.0 5.5 6.9	3.43 0.74 1.04	-28 - 4 92	-13 -20 0	0 -78 -69

Till was obtained from the city of Edmonton, Canada. P_c, a_v and c_v values are taken from the relationships obtained.

From Lambe (27)

Site	Source	c_v (cm²/s)	Settlement (cm) after 18 days ρ	% Variation c_v	ρ
				0% base	
Alibey Dam	Lab. tests	4.8×10^{-4}	30*		
	Field pore-pressure data	120×10^{-4}	55*	2400	83
	Field measurements	—	84**	—	180

* settlement predicted from lab. data and field pore-pressure data
** settlement actually measured in the field

From McGown and Radman (32)

Soil	Specimen Size dia. mm	Effective Stress (kN/m²)	Coefficient of Consolidation c_v (m²/yr)	% Variation c_v
				0% base
Craufurdland clay	254	75	10.5	-38
	152		6.5	-79
	76		2.2	
	254	150	4.5	-57
	152		5.5	-48
	76		2.5	-76

Craufurdland clay is a fissured clay from Kilmarnock, Scotland

From Sarrailh (47)

Soil	Sampler	Preconsolidation Pressure (kPa)	% Variation
St. Alban	100 mm re-shaped*	8.5	0% base
	54 mm standard	7.8	8

St. Alban clay is a sensitive clay from Quebec, Canada

It is noted that the compression index is much smaller for the 100 mm tubes at pressures lower than the preconsolidation pressure and is larger at higher pressures.

* re-shaped sampler is the sampler without internal clearance and which has a tapered length equal to 1/4 (inside diameter)

From Bishop and Al-Dhahir (9)

Soil	P (kN/m^2)	$\Delta P/P$	c_v (m^2/yr) (1) from Δu	(2) from Δv	Ratio (2)/(1)	% Variation in Ratio
Mexico City Clay (A)	19.3	2.0	4.08	3.99[b]	0.97	0% base
	107.5[a]	3.0	0.29	0.46[b]	1.57	61
	513.0[a]	0.15	2.8	0.04[b]	0.014	-98
Brown London Clay	191.7	0.8	0.99	0.67[c]	0.68	-30
	344.7	0.6	0.98	0.52[c]	0.53	-45
	551.6	0.6	0.92	0.41[c]	0.45	-53
Blue London Clay	175.8	1.15	0.31	0.30[c]	0.98	1
	413.7	0.33	0.27	0.21[c]	0.78	-20

A 113mm dia. oedometer employed

a above the preconsolidation load; b using Casagrande's log time method; c fitting at 50% primary volume change

1 c_v determined from dissipation of pore pressure; 2 c_v determined from rate of volume change

specimen size for Brown London Clay and Blue London Clay was 101.6 mm dia. x 101.6 mm high

From Rowe (44)

Soil	Sample	c_v (m²/yr) at stress levels (kN/m²)			% Variation at stress levels (kN/m²)		
		50	100	200	50	100	200
Soft Estuarine Clay	250mm dia. 90 mm thick vertical drainage	35 15×10^3	15 2	5 1.3	1700 7×10^5	1200 67	614 86
	76 mm dia. oedometer	2	1.2	0.7	0% base		
	remoulded 150 mm dia. samples	0.25	0.3	0.7	-88	-75	0

The clay contained organic rootlets.

Principles of Probabilistic Characterization of Soil Properties

Wilson H. Tang[*], M. ASCE

Abstract

Sources of uncertainties affecting characterization of soil properties in a homogeneous soil layer include inherent spatial variability, systematic test bias, random test errors, calibration errors, and estimation error from insufficient samples. These individual contributions are modeled and analyzed with respect to the available data and information. Relevant soil parameters governing most geotechnical performances are spatial average soil properties over some domain of the soil layer. A simplified method is proposed to incorporate the major sources of uncertainties in determining the statistics of these spatial average soil properties. If several independent sources of information are available for estimating a mean soil property, they can be combined to yield the overall statistics. Effect of dependence between sample test values resultant from spatial correlation structure or other systematic error can also be incorporated in the statistical evaluation. The computed statistics of mean soil property may be used for evaluating the reliability of a geotechnical performance or for selecting appropriate design values for soil parameters. It is expected that the proposed probabilistic methodology would yield a more rational and realistic description of the in situ soil properties for further engineering analysis and design.

INTRODUCTION

As long as soil properties are not exactly measured at every point of a soil stratum, it is perhaps convenient to model soil properties probabilistically. Uncertainties associated with prediction of properties for a given soil material may come from various sources. Proper modeling of each component of uncertainties requires first an understanding of its characteristics, whether it would give rise to biased or unbiased estimators, random or systematic error, or subject to spatial variations or averaging over the soil stratum. Further statistical evaluation will be based on available soil exploration and test data augmented by engineering judgment. The objective of this paper is to present a simple methodology for (i) analyzing the major components of uncertainties associated with the prediction of properties for a given soil material and (ii) combining them to obtain the statistics of soil variables that will govern the performance of a geotechnical system. An engineer may use these statistics to select appropriate characteristic soil property values for a conventional deterministic design or to input such statistics into a reliability evaluation of a given geotechnical performance. Only soil properties associated with a homogeneous soil layer are considered. In other words, it is assumed that the soil

[*]Professor of Civil Engineering, University of Illinois at Urbana-Champaign, Illinois

74

profile has been clearly defined for a given soil stratum. Anomalous geological details that have not been detected or located during site exploration are assumed absent.

Geotechnical performances are often governed by spatial average soil properties, such as the average shear strength along a potential sliding surface in slope stability analysis or the average compressibility of a volume of soil beneath a footing in settlement calculation. Sometimes, extreme value (maxima or minima) of local spatial average soil property may govern a system performance; for example, progressive failure of a slope may be initiated by a local zone whose average shear strength is the weakest along a potential sliding surface; whereas, piping failure in an earth dam may depend on the existence of a small zone of highly permeable material. In any event, the spatial average soil property over an appropriate domain (length, area or volume) will be the soil parameter of primary interest.

REVIEW OF RANDOM FIELD MODEL

Most test data on soil properties are obtained for soil specimens, whose physical sizes and locations resemble closely to scattered points in a soil stratum. On the basis of these measured point properties it is necessary to infer the statistics of the spatial average property. Random field modeling of soil properties in a homogeneous stratum (16) provides a mathematically tractable tool to bridge this gap.

Even for a soil layer consisting of only one soil material, natural heterogeneity does exist between points in the supposedly homogeneous layer due to variations in mineral composition, environmental conditions during deposition, past stress history, moisture content and other factors. As a result, soil property is subject to inherent variability, i.e., it varies between points. The discrepancy in soil property between two points in a layer is expected to increase as the two points become further apart. Using a one-dimensional random field model, the spatial average of a statistically homogeneous soil property over a length L can be shown (16,17) to have a mean and variance given by

$$\bar{u}_L = \bar{u} \tag{1}$$

and

$$\tilde{u}_L^2 = [\frac{2}{L} \int_0^L (1 - \frac{\tau}{L})\rho_u(\tau)d\tau]\tilde{u}^2 = \Gamma_u^2(L)\tilde{u}^2 \tag{2}$$

where the model parameters $\bar{u}$, $\tilde{u}$ and $\rho_u(\tau)$ are respectively the mean, standard deviation of the point properties and the correlation coefficient between soil properties at distance τ apart. $\Gamma_u^2(L)$ is the variance function whose value ranges between zero and one. Thus the variance of the spatial average soil property will be generally less than the point variance $\tilde{u}^2$. The amount of reduction increases with L and depends further on the correlation function $\rho_u(\tau)$. Some of the typical one-dimensional correlation and variance functions are summarized in Table 1. A common parameter in these functions is the scale of fluctuation, δ, which may be interpreted as the distance within which soil properties are largely correlated, whereas outside which the soil properties are largely uncorrelated. Sometimes, soil properties may exhibit a mean trend (e.g., with depth). For mathematical convenience, these systematic trends can be identified and separated out first; its contribution can be superimposed later to the results from homogeneous random field model applied to the residual soil properties.

For two- and three-dimensional domains, the variance of spatial average soil property can be expressed again in terms of the point variance $\tilde{u}^2$ multiplied by a variance reduction function $\Gamma_u^2(D)$ where D is the domain to be averaged. Considerable mathematical simplification may result if the multi-dimensional correlation model is of a separable form (e.g., triangular or quadratic exponential correlation function). In such case, the variance function $\Gamma_u^2(D)$ is simply a product of the corresponding one-dimensional variance functions; for example, if domain D denotes an area L_x by L_y, the variance of spatial average property over that area is

$$\tilde{u}_D^2 = \Gamma_u^2(D)\tilde{u}^2 = \Gamma_{ux}^2(L_x)\Gamma_{uy}^2(L_y)\tilde{u}^2 \qquad (3)$$

where $\Gamma_{ux}^2(\ )$ and $\Gamma_{uy}^2(\ )$ are the individual one-dimensional variance functions in x and y directions, respectively.

Geotechnical performance may involve two or more spatial averages of a given soil property. Correlation coefficient between any pair of spatial averages can be determined in terms of variance functions over respective component domains (17). For example, the correlation coefficient between spatial average soil property over length L and that over length L' at distance L_0 apart (see Fig. 1) is given by

$$\rho_{u_L, u_{L'}} = \frac{\sum_{k=0}^{3} (-1)^k L_k^2 \Gamma_u^2(L_k)}{2LL' \Gamma_u(L) \Gamma_u(L')} \qquad (4)$$

where L_k's; k = 0, 1, 2, 3 are the respective geometrical quantities defined in Fig. 1.

COMPONENTS OF UNCERTAINTIES

As indicated earlier, foundation performance is often governed by the spatial average value of the soil property over an appropriate length, area or volume. Three main types of uncertainty may be identified to be associated with this spatial average soil property, namely:

(a) Inherent Variability - As pointed out previously, soil property varies between points even in a homogeneous soil stratum, the spatial average soil property over a given domain will also be subject to uncertainties, although its variability is reduced somewhat from the point variability through the averaging effect.

(b) Statistical Uncertainty - Because of (i) the inherent variability of soil properties within a soil stratum and (ii) the random test and measurement errors associated with most field and laboratory tests, the statistics (such as mean, variance) of a soil property at a point cannot be ascertained with tests on limited number of soil samples. This source of uncertainty is called statistical because it will diminish as the number of test samples becomes large.

(c) Systematic Uncertainties - Mainly contributed by the inability of a test to reproduce the in situ property due to factors such as sample disturbances, size of specimen, different stress conditions, etc. This discrepancy error may not necessarily be reduced through extensive

sampling because the same kind of test conditions is likely to persist
and yield consistently high or low property values. The same applies
to estimating soil property through empirical calibration formulas. The
corresponding calibration error for a particular soil type and site
condition may also be systematic.

A simple model to incorporate each of these uncertainties in the
mean in situ soil property X_I is (15,19)

$$X_I = N_o \, N \, X_A \tag{5}$$

where X_A is the spatial average soil property over an appropriate domain
accounting only for inherent variability; N_o is a correction factor accounting for statistical estimation uncertainty resulting from insufficient samples; N is a correction factor accounting for the systematic
uncertainties resulting from discrepancies between laboratory and in
situ conditions and calibration. N can be further subdivided into component factors N_i's, if necessary, to accommodate various sources of
systematic uncertainties. From a first order analysis (2) the mean and
coefficient of variation (c.o.v.) of X_I becomes

$$\bar{X}_I = \bar{N}_o \, \bar{N} \, \bar{X}_A = \bar{N} \, \bar{x} \tag{6}$$

and

$$\Omega_I = \sqrt{\Delta_o^2 + \Delta_N^2 + \delta_A^2} \tag{7}$$

where the bars denote mean values, δ and Δ's denote c.o.v.'s, $\bar{x}$ is the
mean soil property at a point, $\bar{N}_o$ equals to 1 because only random statistical error is considered in N_o, $\bar{N}$ is the mean bias resulting from
all systematic uncertainties.

Each component of the uncertainty in Eq. 7 can be assessed separately. Based on results of random field model (Eqs. 2 and 3), the
uncertainty due to inherent spatial variability of soil property is

$$\delta_A = \frac{\tilde{x}_A}{\bar{x}_A} = \frac{\Gamma(D) \, \tilde{x}}{\bar{x}} = \Gamma(D) \, \delta \tag{8}$$

where δ is the c.o.v. of soil property at a point, $\tilde{x}_A$ and $\tilde{x}$ are the
standard deviation of X_A and X, respectively, $\Gamma(D)$ is the standard deviation function over domain D (see Table 1). For given inherent variability of a soil property, domain D and correlation characteristics,
δ_A can be assessed accordingly.

The test discrepancy error Δ_N depends on the specific soil property,
site conditions and types of laboratory tests performed. Examples of
uncertainty analysis reported include drained strength parameters (18),
and undrained shear strength (15) associated with slope failures, bearing capacity in sand (4) and relative density of sand (9). An example
of the evaluation of discrepancy between laboratory and in situ undrained shear strength is summarized in Table 2. The overall correction $\bar{N}$
and the test discrepancy error Δ_N can be estimated by combining the
appropriate values of ν_j and Δ_j for a specific clay stratum, namely,

$$\bar{N} = \sum_j \nu_j \tag{9}$$

and

$$\Delta_N = \sqrt{\sum_u \Delta_j^2}$$ (10)

The statistical uncertainty resulting from insufficient samples lies mainly in the estimation of the mean soil property. The methodologies for estimating mean soil property and evaluating the corresponding uncertainty depend on the specific source of data. Assume first that the set of data comes from independent soil samples. For n direct test data x_1, x_2, ..., x_n alone, the estimated mean soil property and its standard deviation are given by

$$\bar{x} = \frac{1}{n} \sum_i x_i$$ (11)

and

$$\tilde{\bar{x}} = \sqrt{\sum_i (x_i - \bar{x})^2/(n-1)} \Big/ \sqrt{n}$$ (12)

For test values calibrated from m indirect tests, the corresponding expressions are

$$\bar{x} = \frac{1}{m} \sum_i x_{ci}$$ (13)

and

$$\tilde{\bar{x}} = \sqrt{[\sum_i (x_{ci} - \bar{x})^2/(m-1)] + \sigma_c^2} \Big/ \sqrt{m}$$ (14)

where x_{ci}'s, i = 1 to m, are the calibrated soil property values from observed indirect test data, σ_c is the standard deviation denoting the random calibration error, which is assumed to be statistically independent between the m calibrations. Any systematic calibration error that exists will be accounted for through the correction factor N in Eq. 5. Lastly, based on experience and judgment of an engineer without the availability of test data, the estimated mean soil property and its standard deviation may be subjectively assessed as $\bar{x} = \mu'$ and $\tilde{\bar{x}} = \sigma'$, respectively. In any event, the c.o.v. denoting contribution from insufficient samples or judgment may be determined from

$$\Delta_o = \frac{\tilde{\bar{x}}}{\bar{x}}$$ (15)

Illustrative Example

The average density over a 10 m deep soil layer, γ_I, is to be estimated on the basis of the following information:

(i) Nine soil samples taken at widely scattered locations have been tested for their densities, which yield a mean of 1800 kg/m^3 and a standard deviation of 200 kg/m^3. Assume random test error to be negligible.

(ii) Assume perfect correlation among soil densities in the horizontal plane but a single exponential correlation model (see Table 1) in the vertical direction with parameter a = 0.3 m.

(iii) From long experience, the densities measured at this laboratory exhibit some discrepancy from those in situ. This systematic bias
could be anywhere between 0.9 to 1.06; that is, the true in situ density
may be anywhere from 90% to 106% of the laboratory measured values.
The c.o.v. denoting the inherent spatial variability between soil density
at points in the given soil layer is $\delta = 200/1800 = 0.111$. The error due
to spatial variability may be computed from Eq. 8 and Table 1 as

$$\delta_A = \frac{0.3}{10} \sqrt{2(\frac{10}{0.3} - 1 + e^{-10/0.3})} \; (0.111) = 0.0268$$

From Eqs. 11, 12 and 15, the error due to insufficient samples is given by

$$\Delta_o = \frac{200/1800}{\sqrt{9}} = 0.0370$$

Lastly, the error due to systematic bias may be evaluated by assuming
the correction factor N to be uniformly distributed between 0.9 and
1.06. According to (2)

$$\bar{N} = \frac{0.9 + 1.06}{2} = 0.98 \qquad \Delta_N = \frac{1}{\sqrt{3}} (\frac{1.06 - 0.9}{1.06 + 0.9}) = 0.0471$$

Incorporating all these component statistics into Eqs. 6 and 7,
the mean and overall c.o.v. of the spatial average density γ_I are

$$\bar{\gamma}_I = 0.98 \times 1800 = 1764 \text{ kg/m}^3$$

and

$$\Omega_I = \sqrt{0.37^2 + 0.0268^2 + 0.0471^2} = 0.0656$$

COMBINING ESTIMATES FROM SEVERAL SOURCES

Several sources of information may be available for estimating a
given soil property. For instance, undrained modulus E_u of a clay may
be estimated from UU, pressuremeter or plate load tests or indirectly
from the undrained strength c_u through the empirical E_u/c_u relationship.
Tests such as UU, field vane and laboratory vane may each be used to
estimate the undrained strength of a marine clay; the undrained strength
may also be estimated indirectly from the effective overburden pressure
p' through the empirical c_u/p' relationship. In a soil exploration program, several kinds of tests may be intentionally run for cross-checking
purposes to obtain information for a single soil property. Moreover,
engineering experiences and judgments have always played a major role in
the estimation of soil property in addition to various test data. It is
thus desirable to develop method for incorporating several sources of
information in estimating a given soil property and to evaluate its
associated error. One such method, which is based on an extension of
earlier work (13,15), is presented as follows.

Suppose several sources of information are available to estimate
the in situ spatial soil property X_I. For each source of information,
the method outlined in previous section may be used to obtain values of
$\bar{X}_I$ and Ω_I according to Eqs. 6 and 7. Inherent spatial variability (as
denoted by δ_A in Eq. 7) is generally not reducible with additional information, whereas the modeling error (as denoted by Δ_o and Δ_N in Eq. 7)
will decrease if additional independent information is available for
estimating the spatial average soil property. It is thus desirable to
treat these two types of uncertainties separately. Suppose analysis of
uncertainty yields the following statistics for the i-th source of
information, namely

$$\bar{X}_{Ii} = \bar{N}_i \; \bar{x} \tag{16}$$

and

$$\Omega_{Ii} = \sqrt{\Delta_i^2 + \delta_A^2} \tag{17}$$

where $\Delta_i^2 = (\Delta_0^2 + \Delta_N^2)_i$. Any two independent sources of information, say i and j, could be combined to yield a weighted average mean bias in the spatial average soil property and the corresponding c.o.v. of such mean bias as

$$\bar{N} = \frac{\bar{N}_i (\Delta_j \; \bar{N}_j)^2 + \bar{N}_j (\Delta_i \; \bar{N}_i)^2}{(\Delta_j \; \bar{N}_j)^2 + (\Delta_i \cdot \bar{N}_i)^2} \tag{18}$$

and

$$\Delta = \frac{1}{\bar{N}} \frac{(\Delta_j \; \bar{N}_j)(\Delta_i \; \bar{N}_i)}{\sqrt{(\Delta_j \; \bar{N}_j)^2 + (\Delta_i \; \bar{N}_i)^2}} \tag{19}$$

Δ will decrease with additional sources of information. Any additional independent source of information could be similarly incorporated one at a time by combining its $\bar{N}_k$ and Δ_k with those obtained from Eqs. 18 and 19 to obtain updated values of $\bar{N}$ and Δ. Final statistics of X_I will be given by

$$\bar{X}_I = \bar{N} \; \bar{x} \tag{20}$$

and

$$\Omega_I = \sqrt{\Delta^2 + \delta_A^2} \tag{21}$$

Observe that $\bar{x}$ is simply an arbitrary reference mean value, say based on one of the sources of information; all the updating in the mean value of X_I is through updating the mean bias $\bar{N}$. Assessment of the quantity δ_A requires the estimation of both the inherent spatial variability and the appropriate correlation (or variance) function (see Eq. 8), which will be presented in a later section.

EFFECT OF CORRELATION BETWEEN SAMPLE VALUES

Aside from systematic test error, the assumption of statistical independence between the observed test values may be violated if the samples are located within closed distances relative to the scale of correlation of the soil property. In terms of estimating the mean soil property over the region, more information is available from samples at wider distance apart than from samples right next to each other since the latter two samples could effectively be considered as coming from one sample. Hence, a weighted sample average should be used to estimate the mean soil property. Baecher (5) suggested the estimated mean soil property to be

$$\hat{x} = \sum_{i=1}^{n} w_i \; x_i \tag{22}$$

where w_i is the weight on the respective sample value x_i, and n is the sample size. The proper set of weights w_i's should

$$\text{minimize Var}(\hat{X}) = \sum_i \sum_j w_i \, w_j \, c_{ij} \, \tilde{x}^2 \qquad (23)$$

subject to the constraints $0 \le w_i \le 1$ and $\sum w_i = 1.0$; and c_{ij} is the correlation coefficient between soil properties at locations i and j. Applying Lagrangian multiplier method yields the following matrix equation

$$\begin{Bmatrix} w^* \\ \lambda \end{Bmatrix} = \begin{bmatrix} C & 1 \\ 1 & 0 \end{bmatrix}^{-1} \begin{Bmatrix} 0 \\ 1 \end{Bmatrix} \qquad (24)$$

from which the proper set of weights w_i^*, i = 1 to n, may be computed. C is the matrix $[c_{ij}]$.

As a numerical example, consider a square sampling grid with nine samples as shown in Fig. 2. Suppose the correlation coefficient between sample i and sample j follows an exponential function as $c_{ij} = \exp(-r_{ij}/a)$ where r_{ij} is the separation distance between samples i and j. Equation 24 yields the set of weights shown in Fig. 2 for a square sampling grid with spacing s = 20 m and 30 m, respectively. Observe that the sample at the center receives the least weight because it is adjacent to the largest number of other samples. As the spacing increases, the effect of correlation decreases, resulting in a narrower range of weights. In the extreme case where the spacing becomes very large, each sample will be assigned the same weight of 1/9 or 0.11. In this example, random test error has been assumed negligible. If random test error is included, the value of c_{ij} will be reduced, thus leading to a more uniform set of relative weights. The estimated mean soil property and its standard deviation (i.e., $\sqrt{\text{Var}(\hat{x})}$) obtained from Eqs. 22 and 23 may be used in place of those previously suggested in Eqs. 11 and 12 for independent samples.

The estimated mean soil property is eventually used to predict geotechnical performance. In some geotechnical problem, the performance is influenced more at some of the sampling locations than others. For example, the settlement of a structure is influenced more by the compressibility of soil close to the surface than that deep underground. Therefore, soil property at the more influential locations should be weighted heavier if all other things are equal. In order to incorporate this location influence effect with the spatial correlations effect the optimal set of weights may be determined to minimize the variance of the predicted performance, namely $\text{Var}[g(\hat{x})]$ where g( ) is the performance function, $\hat{x} = \sum_i w_i \, x_i$ and subject to the same constraints as before (11). This method has been applied to a problem associated with the prediction of the settlement of a pile group resting on a thick layer of normally consolidated clay as shown in Fig. 3. Compression index values have been observed at locations 1, 2 and 3 as indicated. It is desired to determine how these three compression index values should be weighted to obtain the design value of mean compression index for the entire clay layer. Table 3 summarizes the set of optimal weights. If indeed the compression indices between points in the clay layer are uncorrelated and if the compression index at each of the three locations contributes equally to the settlement of the pile group, then the weights should be the same for all three values and equal to 1/3 (as indicated in column two in Table 3). Because of spatial correlation effect exhibited by the point compression index, more weights would be distributed to compression index values x_1 and x_3 relative to x_2 (see column 3). However, the location influence effect would imply the largest weight to x_1 and the smallest weight to x_3, according to the decreasing contributions to the total settlement with depth. These two effects apparently compensate each other at locations 2 and 3 (see column 4). Similar calculations are also performed for a spatial correlation model whose correlation parameter a is only half of that assumed previously. In this case the smaller spatial correlation effect yields a larger overall relative weight for x_2 than x_3 as shown in Table 3.

ESTIMATION FROM CENSORED SAMPLES

A set of sample data may not necessarily be representative of the population being sampled. For instance, if a very weak soil is encountered during sampling, it may be impossible to obtain a specimen; or even if it is obtained, the specimen may be badly disturbed such that testing is useless. For such a specimen, its property will not be known and may be simply ignored in the estimation of soil property based on the rest of the data, thus leading to unconservative estimates of the soil property. For this censored sampling, if it is known that soil property below a certain threshold value x_0 cannot be measured and if the number of such missing samples are carefully recorded, say r_0, then unbiased estimates of the mean and variance can be determined from (11) as

$$\hat{\mu} = \bar{x} - \lambda(\bar{x} - x_0) \tag{25}$$

$$\sigma^2 = s^2 + \lambda(\bar{x} - x_0)^2 \tag{26}$$

where $\bar{x}$ and s^2 are the sample mean and variance of those data actually measured (say with sample size m) and λ depends on the ratio $h = r_0/(r_0 + m)$ and on the ratio $s^2/(\bar{x} - x_0)^2$. A chart for estimating λ is reproduced here in Fig. 4 from (11) for sampling from a normal random variable. When the threshold value is low and when the number of missing samples are small, $\lambda \simeq h$; thus, approximating the unmeasured property values by the threshold values in such case would yield satisfactory estimates. The unbiased estimate of mean soil property in Eq. 25 may be used in place of $\bar{x}$ in Eq. 11 for further statistical evaluations.

Estimation from censored samples can be pursued alternatively using a Bayesian approach. For the above example, the likelihood function is simply

$$L(\text{data}|\theta) = \prod_{i=1}^{m} f(x_i|\theta) \prod_{j=1}^{r_0} \int_{-\infty}^{x_0} f(x|\theta)dx \tag{27}$$

where $f(x_i|\theta)$ is the PDF of the population soil property with parameter θ and evaluated at x_i. The likelihood function may be used to obtain maximum likelihood estimates of θ, or combined with a given prior $f'(\theta)$ to yield posterior estimates of θ (1). Bayesian approach has been used (3,12) to estimate the statistics of trace length of rock joints based on joint traces observed from outcrops in rock. Since it is common that a joint trace may run off the outcrop and thus not completely observable, the actual trace length would be longer than that observed. Another example of censored sampling occurs in the estimation of mean boulder size in a soil stratum from boring log information. Since larger boulders are more likely to be encountered by a boring, the observed samples would tend to be biased towards larger sizes; whereas the measured distance of intersection between a boring and a boulder represents only a chord instead of the full diameter of the boulder (assuming boulders to be spherical) and may thus underestimate the actual boulder size. These two effects of censored sampling should be considered in estimating statistics of boulder sizes.

CORRELATION BETWEEN TWO SPATIAL AVERAGES

Geotechnical performance could involve spatial average properties over several domains. Reliability evaluation requires not only statistics of these individual spatial averages but also a measure of the correlation between pairs of these spatial averages. The correlation can be contributed by the spatial correlation structure of soil properties as modeled earlier by the random fields. Moreover, the common systematic model error as denoted by N_o N in Eq. 5 will affect all the individual spatial averages and thus increase the degree of mutual correlation. Suppose the in situ spatial average soil properties for a pair of domains are modeled following Eq. 5 as

$$X_1 = N_o N X_{A1} \tag{28}$$

$$X_2 = N_o N X_{A2} \tag{29}$$

where X_{A1} and X_{A2} are spatial average soil properties accounting for inherent variability; N_o N are systematic modeling error assumed to be the same for the two cases. The correlation coefficient between X_1 and X_2 can be derived using algebra of expected values (1) as

$$\rho_{X_1,X_2} = \frac{\rho \, \delta_{A1} \, \delta_{A2} + \Delta^2 + \rho \, \delta_{A1} \, \delta_{A2} \, \Delta^2}{\sqrt{\Delta^2 + \delta_{A1}^2} \, \sqrt{\Delta^2 + \delta_{A2}^2}}$$

where δ_{A1}, δ_{A2} and Δ are c.o.v.'s as defined in Eqs. 17 and 21; ρ is the correlation coefficient between the two spatial averages contributed by the random field model (Eq. 4). As the inherent variability is much smaller than the modeling error, i.e., δ/Δ approaches zero, ρ_{X_1,X_2} approaches 1 denoting perfect correlation; whereas for a small modeling error (i.e., $\Delta \to 0$), ρ_{X_1,X_2} reduces to that contributed by inherent spatial correlation only, namely ρ.

ESTIMATION OF INHERENT VARIABILITY AND AUTOCOVARIANCE FUNCTIONS

The inherent variability of soil property at a point may be estimated by calculating the sample variance of a set of soil property values observed at scattered locations throughout the stratum. However, the observed soil property value is subject to two kinds of random errors (aside from systematic test discrepancies), namely the inherent spatial variability and random testing error. The random testing error may be reduced by repeating tests on soil samples collected at one location. Fortunately, the testing error is generally only a fraction (20 to 50%) of the inherent spatial variability (10); hence, a large part of the testing error could be removed through few test replications. Observing that random test errors are statistically independent between sample test values, whereas spatial variability of soil properties are subject to

possible correlation structure, Baecher (6) suggested alternatively that
the component variance pertaining to testing error may be evaluated from
the difference of the observed autocovariance functions at the origin
and that extrapolated from the rest of the observed autocovariance functions as indicated in Fig. 4. Although mean soil property values can
vary between sites, inherent variability may be relatively constant.
Typical c.o.v. for various soil properties have been collected and
summarized in (4).

The estimation of the autocovariance function or the correlation
structure of soil property in a homogeneous stratum generally requires
a large number of test samples at various distances apart, including
samples located sufficiently close together. For a set of uniformly
spaced measurements on a line, the sampling variance of estimator for
the correlation function has been widely studied (6). In most site
exploration programs, measurements may be taken at non-uniformly spaced
locations. In such case, a practical procedure of estimating the correlation function is to divide the separation distances between pairs
of sample values into discrete intervals, and then calculate the correlation coefficient for all pairs of sample values within each interval.
An example of fitting a correlation model to calibrated skirt penetration resistance values observed at a platform site in the North Sea is
shown in Fig. 5. The error in the estimated correlation coefficient
could be significant if the distances between measured locations deviate considerably from the discretized average distance for each interval. Moreover, for small sample size, the estimated values are generally
lower than the actual correlation coefficients and could become negative
even though actual correlation coefficients are positive (7). Various
researchers (4,7,11,16) have also suggested methodologies for assessing
correlation function from observed data. Nevertheless, the exact form
of a correlation function may not be significant for most practical
application. The correlation parameter δ (see Table 1) may well be a
sufficient parameter to capture the spatial correlation structure.
Typical correlation parameters for various soil properties reported in
the literature have been summarized in (4).

PROBABILITY DISTRIBUTION OF SOIL PROPERTY

Observed soil property values may be plotted in probability papers
to infer the true probability distribution of the soil property. Based
on a detailed literature search, Baecher, et al. (4) summarized the
probability distributions that have been empirically determined for various soil properties. Since these property values are measured from
test specimen, the distribution obtained is basically that for the soil
property at a given point. Such information is not as useful as it may
appear because geotechnical performance is often controlled by the average soil property over some spatial domain instead of the soil property at a point. For large domain, the spatial average soil property
is expected to be approaching the normal distribution according to the
Central Limit Theorem regardless of the probability distribution for
soil property at a point. On the other hand, geotechnical performance
may be controlled by extreme value (largest or smallest) of local average soil property. In this case, statistical theory of extremes (2) or
theory of random process and random field (17) would be helpful in
determining the type of distribution for the extreme values.

CONCLUSION

Various sources of uncertainties affecting the mean soil property are identified. Simple methodologies to model, analyze and combine individual uncertainty components in the determination of statistics of the average soil properties over some appropriate spatial domains have been proposed. The case of availability of multiple information sources for estimating a given soil property and the effect of possible dependence between sample test values on statistical evaluation of mean soil properties are also studied.

The statistics of mean soil property derived above may be used as inputs to subsequent reliability evaluation of geotechnical performances or as basis for selection of characteristic soil property values for geotechnical design. It is expected that the proposed methodology for probabilistic characterization of soil properties would yield a more rational and realistic description of the in situ soil properties for further engineering analysis and design.

Appendix: References

1. Ang, A. H-S. and W. H. Tang, Probability Concepts in Engineering Planning and Design, V. I, Basic Principles, John Wiley and Sons, New York, 1975.

2. Ang, A. H-S. and W. H. Tang, Probability Concepts in Engineering Planning and Design, V. II: Decision, Risk and Reliability, John Wiley and Sons, New York, 1984.

3. Baecher, G. B., "Progressively Censored Sampling of Rock Joint Traces," Mathematical Geology, Vol. 12, 1980, pp. 33-40.

4. Baecher, G. B., Chen, M., Ingra, T. S., Lee, T. and L. R. Nucci, "Geotechnical Reliability of Offshore Gravity Platforms," Report MITSG 80-20, Sea Grant Program, Massachusetts Institute of Technology, Cambridge, Mass., 1980.

5. Baecher, G. B., "Optimal Estimators for Soil Properties," Journal of the Geotechnical Engineering Division, ASCE, Vol. 107, No. GT5, May 1981.

6. Baecher, G. B., "Simplified Geotechnical Data Analysis." Notes for NATO Advanced Study Institute on Structural and Geotechnical Reliability, RONNE, Denmark, August 1982.

7. Baecher, G. B., "On Estimating Autocovariance of Soil Properties," Proceedings of 4th ASCE Specialty Conference on Probabilistic Mechanics and Structural Reliability, Jan. 1984, Berkeley, pp. 214-218.

8. Bartlett, M. S., "On the Theoretical Specification and Sampling Properties of Autocorrelated Time-Series," Suppl. Journal of Royal Statistical Society, Vol. 8 (27), 1946.

9. Halder, A. and W. H. Tang, "Uncertainty Analysis of Relative Density," Journal of the Geotechnical Engineering Division, Proc. ASCE, Vol. 105, No. GT7, July 1979, pp. 899-904.

10. Lumb, P., "Precision and Accuracy of Soil Tests," Statistics and Probability in Civil Engineering, P. Lumb, ed., Hong Kong University Press, Hong Kong, 1971, pp. 329-346.

11. Lumb, P., "Application of Statistics in Soil Mechanics," in Soil Mechanics-New Horizons, I. K. Lee, ed., Newnes-Butterworths Co., 1974, pp. 44-111.

12. Priest, S. D. and J. A. Hudson, "Estimation of Discontinuity Spacing and Trace Length Using Scanline Surveys," Int. Journal of Rock Mechanics Min. Sci. and Geomech. Absts., Vol. 18, pp. 183-197, 1981.

13. Tang, W. H., "A Bayesian Evaluation of Information for Foundation Engineering Design," Statistics and Probability of Civil Engineering, P. Lumb, ed., Hong Kong University Press, Hong Kong, 1971, pp. 173-186.

14. Tang, W. H., "Probabilistic Evaluation of Penetration Resistances," Journal of the Geotechnical Engineering Division, ASCE, Vol. 105, No. GT10, 1979, pp. 1173-1191.

15. Tang, W. H., Yucemen, M. S. and A. H-S. Ang, "Probability-Based Short Term Design of Soil Slopes," Canadian Geotechnical Journal, Vol. 13, 1976, pp. 201-215.

16. Vanmarcke, E. H., "Probabilistic Modeling of Soil Profiles," Journal of the Geotechnical Engineering Division, ASCE, Vol. 103, No. GT11, November 1977, pp. 1237-1246.

17. Vanmarcke, E. H., Random Fields: Analysis and Synthesis, M.I.T. Press, Cambridge, Mass., 1983.

18. Yucemen, M. S. and W. H. Tang, "Long-Term Stability of Soil Slopes-- A Reliability Approach," Proc., 2nd ICASP, Aachen, Germany, Sept. 1975.

19. Yucemen, M. S., Tang, W. H. and A. H-S. Ang, "A Probabilistic Study of Safety and Design on Earth Slopes," SRS No. 402, University of Illinois, Civil Engineering Studies, Urbana, July 1973.

TABLE 1   Formula of Typical Variance Functions
(based on results in 17)

Correlation Function $\rho_u(\tau)$		Variance Function $\Gamma_u^2(L)$
Single Exponential ($a = \delta/2$)	$e^{-\tau/a}$	$\frac{2a^2}{L^2}(\frac{L}{a} - 1 + e^{-L/a})$
Quadratic Exponential ($b = \delta/\sqrt{\pi}$)	$e^{-(\tau/b)^2}$	$(\frac{b}{L})^2[\frac{L}{b}\sqrt{\pi}\,\text{erf}(\frac{L}{b})-1+e^{-(L/b)^2}]$
Uniform 1	$1\ ;\ \tau \leq \delta$ $0\ ;\ \tau > \delta$	$1\ ;\ L \leq \delta$ $\delta/L\ ;\ L > \delta$
Uniform 2	$1\ ;\ \tau \leq \delta/2$ $0\ ;\ \tau > \delta/2$	$1\quad ;\ L \leq \delta/2$ $\frac{\delta}{L}(1 - \frac{\delta}{4L})\ ;\ L > \delta/2$
Triangular	$1-\tau/\delta\ ;\ \tau \leq \delta$ $0\ ;\ \tau > \delta$	$1 - L/3\delta\ ;\ L \leq \delta$ $\frac{\delta}{L}(1 - \frac{\delta}{3L})\ ;\ L > \delta$

TABLE 2   Summary of Test Discrepancy Factors (from 2)

Factor	Effect	Soil Type	Range	Mean Bias ν_j	Test Discrepancy Error Δ_j
N_1	Change in stress state	Low sensitivity ($s_t = 1 - 2$)	1.0 - 1.1	1.03	0.02
		Medium sensitivity ($s_t = 2 - 4$)		1.05	0.02
		Sensitive ($s_t = 4 - 8$)		1.07	0.02
		Unknown sensitivity ($s_t = 1 - 8$)		1.05	0.03
N_2	Mechanical disturbance	Shelby tube specimen	1.0 - 1.6	1.3	0.13
		Bore hole specimen	1.15 - 2.25	1.7	0.19
N_3	Size of specimen	Stiff-fissured clay	0.55 - 0.85	0.70	0.12
		Intact clay	0.85 - 1.00	0.93	0.05
N_4	Rate of shearing	Slightly sensitive to sensitive (strength reduction 3-10% per log increment of time)	0.6 - 1.0	0.80	0.14
		Very sensitive (10 - 14%)	0.45 - 0.7	0.58	0.12
		Unknown sensitivity (3 - 14%)	0.45 - 1.0	0.73	0.22
N_5	Sample orientation and anisotropy	Isotropic	0.97 - 1.08	1.0	0.03
		C-anisotropy	0.85 - 1.20	1.03	0.10
		M-anisotropy	0.8 - 1.0	0.9	0.06
N_6	Plane strain failure	All soil types	1.0 - 1.1	1.05	0.03
N_7	Progressive failure	Stiff clay	0.9 - 1.0	0.93	0.03
		Medium clay		0.97	0.03

TABLE 3   Summary of Relative Weights

	Uncorrelated Field, No Influence Effect on Settlement	Spatial Correlation Effect Only	Correlation Effect and Influence Effect On Settlement
x_1	0.33	0.38	0.55
x_2	0.33	0.24	0.23
x_3	0.33	0.38	0.22
		a = 10 ft.	
x_1	0.33	0.35	0.50
x_2	0.33	0.30	0.30
x_3	0.33	0.35	0.20
		a = 5 ft.	

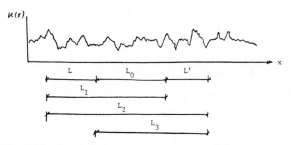

Figure 1   Spatial Average Over Respective Distances

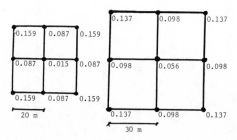

Figure 2   Relative Weights for Square Sampling Grid

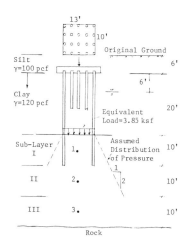

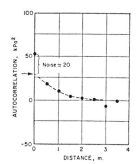

Figure 3 Pile Foundation on
          Compressible Clay
          Stratum

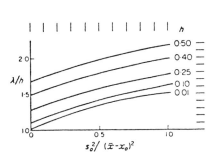

Figure 4 λ Factor for Censored
          Samples (from Ref. 11)

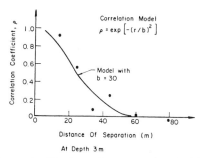

Figure 5 Procedure for Esti-
          mating Random Test
          Error (from Ref. 7)

Figure 6 Fitting of Correlation Model
          to Observed Penetration Re-
          sistance at Depth 3 m (Brent
          D) (from Ref. 14)

Application of Methods of Probabilistic
Characterization of Soil Properties

Loren R. Anderson[1], M. ASCE; Kevan D. Sharp[2], A.M. ASCE;
David S. Bowles[3], M. ASCE; and Ronald V. Canfield[4]

ABSTRACT

     The use of probabilistic methods to describe soil properties has
many applications. One such application that has been developed is in
the area of probabilistic slope stability analysis. A model based on
some of the factors of uncertainty of slope stability analysis and its
application as a tool to assess the reliability of existing embankments
and as a design tool is discussed. A comparison is made with a
conventional subsurface investigation and one which is designed to
acquire the probabilistic soil parameters. The methodology which has
been applied to tailings embankments is discussed.

INTRODUCTION

     Regardless of the care taken in the siting, design, and
construction of an earth dam or some other type of civil works
structures, some residual level of risk of a catastrophic failure will
remain. The event that causes the failure may be of natural origin such
as a flood, or an earthquake, it may be related to the structure itself
such as uneven settlement, core cracking, piping or embankment or
foundation slips, or to human related factors such as incorrect
operation or acts of war.

     An outcome of the Teton Dam failure of June 5, 1976, was the
realization that the civil engineering profession has fallen behind
other engineering disciplines in the application of risk and the
procedures developed for risk analysis in the manufacturing industries,
where many identical items are produced under conditions which are
conducive to strict quality control, are generally not applicable to
civil engineering projects.

[1]Professor of Civil Engineering and Associate Dean of Engineering. UMC
41, Utah State University, Logan, UT 84322.
[2]Research Assistant Professor of Civil Engineering. UMC 41, Utah State
University, Logan, UT 84322.
[3]Research Professor of Civil Engineering. UMC 41, Utah State
University, Logan, UT 84322.
[4]Professor of Applied Statistics. UMC 42, Utah State University, Logan,
UT 84322.

The successful practice of geotechnical engineering in general and earth dam design in particular requires judgment that is based on a knowledge of precedent as well as an understanding of the principles of soil mechanics and geology (Peck, 11). The fact is often used to support the argument that risk analysis and probabilistic methods have no place in geotechnical engineering. The opposite conclusion should be reached. Probabilisitic methods and risk analysis have been developed specifically to cope with uncertainty in a rational way. Risk analysis procedures can be useful even when the design involves making many decisions for which some are based on analytical procedures, some on empirical procedures, some using precedent based design rules and some using strictly engineering judgment. Probabilistic methods are available that can consider uncertainty involving a judgment decision and include it in the same probabilistic analysis that considers the uncertainty in an analytically based decision.

A major area of geotechnical engineering for which the utilization of risk-based analysis procedures would be helpful is that of alternative selection, whether it be for selecting alternative designs or for selecting alternative methods for mitigating a hazard. In the case of selecting an alternative, the problem involves evaluating the relative risk of the alternatives rather than the absolute risk. Bowles et al. (5) suggest that as an aid in selecting alternatives, risk analysis can be applied at all stages of project development from the initial feasibility studies through construction and into operation and maintentance. As the project progresses the data base for making risk assessment grows and the ability to evaluate risk increases. It is not likely that an absolute assessment of risk for a project as complex as an earthdam will be possible for some time, if ever. However, a relative assessment of risk is all that is needed for selecting the best alternatives. It can help an experienced engineer determine whether an investment to improve one part of a complex structure will significantly reduce the overall probability of failure of the structure. Bowles et al. (6) suggested the method shown in Figure 1 as a risk-based method for establishing priorities for alternative dam safety improvements.

The first step in developing full risk analysis procedures for civil works projects is to individually develop and apply probabilistic techniques to the various analysis and design activities. For an earth dam project a logical place to start is with slope stability analysis. Even though slope stability of the embankment has rarely been the direct cause of a major failure, there are a number of reasons to select slope stability as a starting point for probabilistic analysis.

● Slope stability analysis is based on an analytical method that can be adapted to probabilistic analysis and it is a more straightforward place to start than with less understood phenomena such as piping.
● The probabilistic slope stability procedures can also be applied to the more important design consideration of foundation stability.
● Probabilistic slope stability analysis requires consideration of the spatial variability of soil properties which is important for many other geotechnical engineering problems.

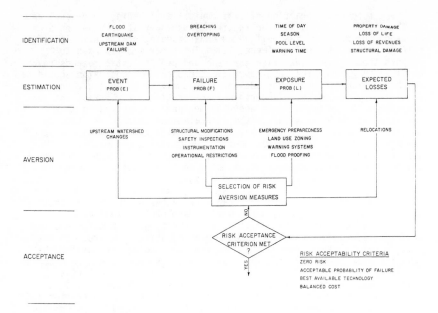

Figure 1. Risk-Based Method for Establishing Priorities for Alternative Dam Safety Improvements.

PROBABILISTIC SLOPE STABILITY ANALYSIS

Uncertainties in Slope Stability Analysis

There are several sources on uncertainty that are associated with assessing slope stability. Conventional deterministic slope stability analysis cannot rationally assess these factors in the way that probabilistic analysis does. These uncertainties include:

● Approximation in describing the geometry of the embankment.
● Errors in estimating pore pressures.
● Spatial variability in shear strength, and measurements and sampling errors in field measurements of shear strength.
● Inaccuracies in the mechanics of the slope stability model.

Anderson et al. (2) have developed a methodology for probabilistic assessment of embankment stability and have addressed some of these sources of uncertainty.

Embankment Geometry. The geometry of the embankment and variability of soil density have been shown to have negligible effect on embankment reliabiity. In the methodology presented by Anderson et al. (2) they have been treated deterministically. Alonso (1) shows that probabilisitic consideration of the density and geometry do not greatly

influence embankment reliability because they occur in both the
resisting moment and driving moment in the limiting equilibrium
equations and their effects tend to cancel.

Pore Pressure. Uncertainty in the distribution of pore pressure
can result from spatial variability and uncertainty in the permeability
of the embankment soil, fluctuation in the phreatic surface due to
variations in the reservoir level or variations in drawdown rates. At
this time an efficient method to probabilistically characterize the
spatial variability of pore pressure has not been developed. Research
at Utah State University (3,4) investigated pore pressure as a random
variable for probabilistic slope stability analysis during steady state
seepage. Pore pressure uncertainty was attributed to the spatial
variability of permeability. A Monte Carlo technique was required to
assess the probability of failure. This type of solution is generally
expensive and not practical for routine applications.

Anderson et al. (2) treat pore pressure as a deterministic
quantity. By computing the probability of failure for various pore
pressure conditions a critical pore pressure state can be defined as the
pore pressure condition that results in an unacceptable probability of
failure. Pore pressures in the structure can then be monitored and
compared with the critical pore pressure state. If a critical condition
is approached, appropriate remedial measures can be taken.

Spatial Variability of Soil Parameters. Vanmarcke (14) suggests
three major sources of uncertainty in soil profile modeling for the
purpose of describing spatial variation of soil parameters:

● natural heterogeneity
● limited information about subsurface conditions
● measurement errors

Natural heterogeneity refers to the actual spatial variation of the
shear strength of the material and must be estimated to properly
evaluate the probability of a slope failure. For constructed slopes,
natural heterogeneity will be modfied by construction methods. The
accuracy of the spatial variation estimate depends on the extent of the
subsurface investigation and the accuracy of the measurements (the
second and third error sources listed above). Judgment must be
exercised in planning the subsurface investigation in order to trade off
between the number and location of soundings and the value of obtaining
the information.

Even when using the best available techniques to sample and measure
the soil parameters, measurement errors will be present and these could
include a measurement bias. If an estimate of the bias can be made, the
mean values of the soil parameters should be adjusted accordingly. When
using an indirect method such as a cone penetrometer to evaluate shear
strength, the uncertainty involved in making the conversion from the
penetration resistance to shear strength will introduce an additional
measurement error.

Model Error. Model error depends on the method of deterministic slope stability analysis and the assumptions that must be made to make the analysis statically determinant. Whitman and Bailey (16) suggest that the plane strain safety factor computed by Bishop's simplified method may be in error by as much as five percent. It is generally accepted that all slope stability analysis methods make conservative assumptions. Thus the actual safety factor is greater than the analysis indicates. One of the difficulties in error analysis is in separating this bias from random error. The magnitude of the bias varies for each individual case, depending on the particular slope geometry, failure surface, soil conditions and pore pressure conditions. Thus this bias may be considered to be a random variable which can be described by a probability density function having positive skew, such as the beta distribution. Cornell (7) has suggested that the variance of the safety factor can be written as a combination of the variance due to model error and the variance due to spatial variability of the resisting moment as follows:

$$\bar{F}^2 = (V_F \bar{F}_e)^2 + \bar{F}_s^2 \tag{1}$$

in which

$\quad V_F =$ the coefficient of variation of the plane strain safety
         factor, F_e due to model error
$\quad \bar{F}_s^2 =$ the variance of safety factor which includes the spatial
         variability of shear strength
$\quad \bar{F}^2 =$ the total variance of the safety factor

Probabilistic Slope Stability Model

Probabilistic analysis of embankment safety requires a reorientation of thinking with respect to safety factor. The term "safety factor" lacks precise definition in a probabilistic context. In a deterministic analysis, pessimistically selected strength parameters are used to compute a safety factor that is considered to be representative of the whole embankment regardless of size. In the more realistic probability model, the safety factor is variable and changes from point to point throughout the embankment. Only when the average value of the safety factor falls below 1.0 over a sufficiently large section of the embankment can failure occur.

Vanmarcke (14) introduced a total stress probabilisitic slope stability model that considers a cylindrical failure surface of variable length as shown in Figure 2. The mechanics of this model are two dimensional because in the stability analysis the length of the cylinder cancels. However, the statistical variation in shear strength is considered over the entire failure surface; hence, a three dimensional spatial variation of shear strength is included in the analysis. Anderson et al. (2) developed an effective stress analysis model based on the failure surface of Figure 2 that would accommodate zoned embankments and stratified foundations. In this model statistical strength parameters are required for each separately identifiable zone or stratum.

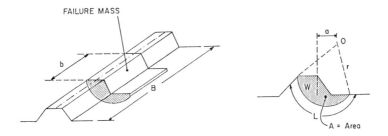

Figure 2a. Typical Cylindrical   Figure 2b. Typical Cross-Section of
Failure Mass of an Earth Embankment   Failure Mass
(after Vanmarcke 15)   (after Vanmarcke 15)

Probability of Failure

    The probability of failure occurring along an assumed cylindrical
failure surface such as that shown in Figure 2 is defined as the
probability of the safety factor being less than 1.0. The probability
of the safety factor being less than 1.0 is graphically shown in Figure
3 as the area under the probability density function of the safety
factor where F_b is less than 1.0, written prob(F<1.0). This area can be
computed from the mean and standard deviation of the safety factor for
the assumed failure surface and for an assumed functional form of the
probability density function. In the model, a Gaussian distribution is
used for the safety factor and its use is justified by the Central Limit
Theorem. The mean and standard deviation of the safety factor are
calculated using Equations 2 and 3, respectively, as described below.

    The probability of failure for a specific assumed failure surface
is a function of the mean safety factor and the standard deviation of
the safety factor. The mean safety factor can be defined as,

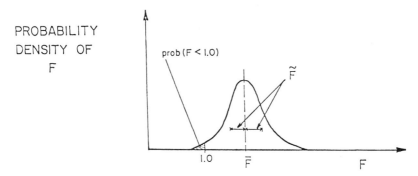

Figure 3. Probability Density of Safety Factor.

$$F_b = \frac{br\Sigma \bar{s}_{bj}L_j + R_e}{bM_o} \qquad (2)$$

where
b = width of the failure surface (Figure 2)
r = radius of the failure cylinder
$\bar{s}_{bj}$ = average shear strength of the j_{th} zone over the cylinder failure width b
L_j = arc length of the failure surface over the j_{th} zone
R_e = end resistance to failure
M_o = overturning moment

In calculating the standard deviation of the safety factor, $\tilde{F}_b$, only the shear strength, with its components of cohesion and friction, is considered to be a random variable. The density, embankment geometry, and pore pressure are assumed to be deterministic. Furthermore, the variance of the resisting end moment, R_e, is neglected. Assuming the strength parameters of various soil types in an embankment to be statistically independent, the standard deviation of the safety factor can be expressed as:

$$\tilde{F}_b = \frac{r\sqrt{\Sigma \tilde{s}^2_{bj}L^2_j}}{M_o} \qquad (3)$$

where

$\tilde{s}^2_{bj}$ = variance of shear strength of the j_{th} zone over cylinder failure width b.

As shown by Equations 2 and 3 the mean and standard deviation of the safety factor are in turn respectively functions of the mean and standard deviation of the shear strength of the soil in each zone of stratum. The mean shear strength $\bar{s}_{bj}$ for each zone or stratum is simply the mean of a statistically significant number of shear strength measurements, made at random locations along the failure surface and within the appropriate zone or stratum. The shear strength is generally described in terms of its cohension and friction components c and $\sigma\tan\phi$. Anderson et al. (2) conservatively assume these components to be independent. Therefore, the standard deviation of the shear strength can be expressed as,

$$\tilde{s}_{bj} = \{\tilde{c}^2_{bj} + (\sigma \widetilde{\tan\phi})^2_{bj}\}^{1/2} \qquad (4)$$

In this equation the ~ sign is used to indicate standard deviation and

s = shear strength
c = cohension
σ = effective stress
ϕ = friction angle

The subscripts will be explained below.

Spatial Variation of Shear Strength. Variations in shear strength
occur naturally in a soil mass, however, the stability of an embankment
is not affected by very small areas of weakness because these are
compensated for by the strength of adjacent areas. Thus, local
weaknesses tend to be "averaged out" when the strength of a larger area
is considered, even though the point-to-point variation in the shear
strength can be quite high. There may be several places in the soil
mass where the strength is low or high but only for a short distance.
If the average strength is calculated over an interval of length b which
is moved along the axis of the embankment, this is referred to as the
moving average of the point values of shear strength in soil j, s_j. The
variance of this moving average is less than the variance of the point
strength values. Consequently, the standard deviation of the average
values, $\tilde{s}_{bj}$, is less than the standard deviation of the point
values, $\tilde{s}_j$. As the averaging length Δb is increased, the standard
deviation of the average shear strengths decreases. It is the value of
the shear strength average over the failure surface and not the local
weak or strong values which are important for determining the safety
factor. It follows that it is the standard deviation associated with
the average shear strength over the failure surface of length b and arc
length L_j of Figure 2 which is needed in Equation 4 and not the standard
deviation of the point strength values.

Vanmarcke (15) showed that the standard deviation of shear
strength, $\tilde{s}_{bj}$, by variance reduction functions, as follows:

$$\tilde{s}_{bj} = \{\Gamma_{s,z}(b)\}_j \{\Gamma_{s,1}(L)\} \tilde{s}_j \qquad (5)$$

in which

$\{\Gamma_{s,z}(b)\}_j$ = shear strength variance function along the embankment
axis for the j_{th} soil type

$\{\Gamma_{s,1}(L)\}_j$ = shear strength variance function along the arc of the
failure surface for the j_{th} soil type

For a soil with both cohesion and friction components, the variance
and variance reduction functions must of course be stated in terms of
cohesion and friction. The variance of the shear strength of the jth
soil can be expressed as follows:

$$\tilde{s}_{bj}^2 = \{\Gamma_{c,z}(b)\}_j^2 \{\Gamma_{c,\ell}(L)\}_j^2 \tilde{c}_j^2$$

$$+ \{\Gamma_{\tan\phi,z}(b)\}_j^2 \{\Gamma_{\tan\phi,\ell}(L)\}_j^2 (\tan\phi)_j^2 \qquad (6)$$

Evaluation of the variance functions along the arc length is not
convenient since spatial variance reduction functions are measured in
terms of cartesian coordinates. This requires that the variance
reduction functions in the x and y directions be transformed to a
reduction function along the failure arc. This transformation has been
developed in Sharp et al. (13) and Anderson et al. (2).

As shown by Equation 6, an evaluation of the standard deviation of the safety factor (Equation 3) depends not only on the point standard deviation of the shear strength but also on the variance reduction functions for each component of shear strength.

Variance Reduction and Autocorrelation Functions. Equation 6 involves two variance reduction functions for each soil property. These reduction functions are functions of the autocorrelation functions $\rho_x(\cdot), \rho_y(\cdot)$, and $\rho_z(\cdot)$ and are derived in Anderson et al. (2). Each autocorrelation function in effect describes the rate of fluctuatio of a spatially distributed random variable about its mean. If correlation remains high over a long distance, the rate of fluctuation is low and vice versa.

SUBSURFACE INVESTIGATION

The subsurface investigation for the design of a proposed earth dam structure or for the evaluation of an existing earth structure has a number of purposes only some of which are related to developing the necessary parameters for a slope stability analysis. Information must be obtained for many analysis and design activities associated with the dam embankments and foundation such as slope stability, seepage, foundation dewatering, and grouting requirements. The availability and the quality of the core, shell and filter material must be determined. Locations for the spillway and outlet works must also be selected. Keeping in mind that a subsurface investigation must satisfy many purposes a comparison between the subsurface investigations required to determine the various parameters for conventional and probabilistic slope stability analysis of an existing structure will be made.

Conventional Stability Analysis

In order to conduct a conventional slope stability analysis for an existing structure the following information is required.

- A geometric definition of the embankment section including zones.
- A definition of the foundation conditions.
- A description of existing and projected pore pressure conditions in the embankment and the foundation.
- A determination of shear strength, unit weight and permeability parameters for the embankment and foundation material.

In determining the strength parameters for analysis, laboratory and/or field tests are performed on representative samples of each material judged to be important for slope stability analysis. The strength parameters are then pessimistically selected for use in the analysis. The number, depth and type of borings that are required for the investigation depend on the length, height and complexity of the embankment, the nature of the foundation materials and the general topographic relief at the site. In general, however, three or four borings would be used to define a section at several locations along the length of the embankment.

Probabilistic Stability Analysis

In conducting a probabilistic slope stability analysis the same general purposes that were listed for a conventional analysis are applicable for the probabilistic analysis. However, a much more detailed (and extensive) investigation is required to determine the appropriate statistical strength parameters. From equations 2, 3 and 6 it can be shown that the following statistical strength parameters are required for such a probabilistic slope stability analysis:

- Mean values for both cohesion and $\tan\phi$ for all zones that could influence the stability.
- Point variance (or standard deviation) values for both cohesion and $\tan\phi$ for all zones that could influence the stability.
- Autocorrelation functions in each of the three coordinate directions for both cohesion and $\tan\phi$ for all zones that could influence the stability.

The determination of the mean and point variance (or standard deviation) for each strength component of each material could generally be done using essentially the same number of borings that are required for a conventional analysis. More actual laboratory or field tests, however, would probably be required to have a sufficient sample size. The major difference in the subsurface investigation requirements between a conventional and a probabilistic analysis is in the additional information required to determine the autocorrelation functions in each coordinate direction for each strength component of each material.

Utah State University has conducted probabilisitic slope stability analysis of two different existing tailings dams located near Miami, Arizona. Figures 4 and 5 show the layout of conventional borings and

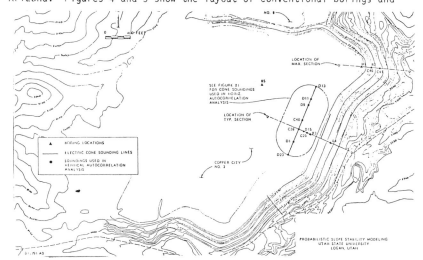

Figure 4. Site Plan of Copper City Tailings Dam No. 2.

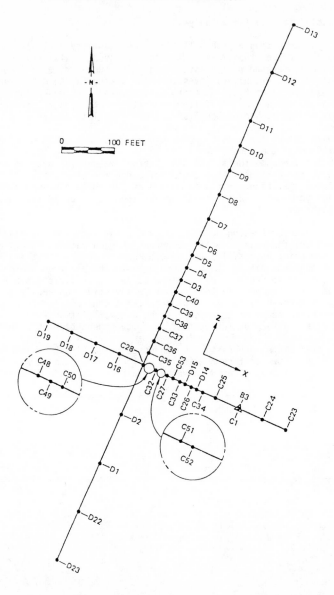

Figure 5.   Cone Sounding Location for Horizontal Autocorrelation Analysis

cone penetrometer soundings that were required for one of the projects.

Conventional methods of performing subsurface investigations (drilling and sampling for laboratory testing) not practical to economically develop the required probabilistic parameters. The electric cone penetrometer was used by the Utah State University team and appears to be an excellent way to develop the necessary data. The electric cone penetrometer indirectly provides strength data at 0.125 ft depth intervals, and under ideal conditions up to 600 to 800 ft of soundings can be obtained per day in tailings material. By properly spacing the penetrometer soundings, the required parameters for the probabilistic slope stability analysis were obtained. Since the cone penetrometer does not retrieve a sample, it was necessary to make several conventional solid borings to obtain samples for classifying the soil and for performing shear tests that were used to calibrate the cone penetrometer.

Conversion of Cone Bearing to Strength. In order to perform the required statistical data analysis using the cone penetrometer the cone pentrometer data must be converted to the appropriate strength parameters. Schmertmann (12), Mitchell and Lunne (10), Harr (8), and Jones and Van Zyl (9) discuss the conversion of cone penetrometer data to strength parameters. There are some questions in interpreting the cone penetration data because of uncertainty in the failure mechanism and the zone of influence of the cone as it advances through the stratified tailings deposits, and because of the influence of the water table on the response of the cone. Furthermore, there is some uncertainty in converting cone bearing resistance to strength parameters even when laboratory data are available for correlating cone bearing resistance and strength parameters. These uncertainties should be included in the probabilistic analysis. The methodology developed by Anderson et al. (2) accounts for these uncertainties in estimating the probabilistic parameters. The two tailings embankment dams that were studied by the Utah State University team were cohesionless and the cone bearing conversion considered only the frictional compontent ($\tan\phi$).

Mean and Point Variance. The estimates of the mean and variance of shear strength, $\bar{s}$ and $\bar{s}^2$, must be representative of the soil type throughout the entire embankment. Thus, portions of the digitized records of representative penetrometer soundings should be pooled to compute a representative mean and variance. Portions of the records that are pooled must be from the same identifiable soil type and, in order to avoid unrepresentative results, soundings should not be concentrated in a small area of the embankment. Pooling can then be performed for each soil type identified in the embankment profile. Additionally, tests can be performed on strength data obtained from each soil type to determine if each is statistically different in terms of mean and variance.

The documentation of a computer program for computing the mean and point variance of $\tan\phi$ from cone penetrometer soundings in presented by Anderson et al. (2).

Horizontal Autocorrelation. Horizontal autocorrelations may be
estimated from the data derived by placing a series of soundings at
constant spacing perpendicular to (x direction) parallel with the
embankment axis (z direction). The placement of the lines of soundings
must be located such that the x and z autocorrelations can be determined
for each soil type in the embankment section.

The x and z autocorrelograms can be computed by considering the
values of shear strength along lines at constant elevation in the x and
z directions, respectively. Estimates of autocorrelation functions can
be improved by pooling autocorrelation estimates from successive
elevations separated by a predetermined vertical distance. Documentaion
of a computer program for estimating horizontal autocorrelation
functions from in situ strength measurements is presented by Anderson et
al. (2).

The layout of soundings for estimating horizontal autocorrelations
must be carefully selected. Since the autocorrelogram decays rapidly at
short lag distances and more slowly with increasing lag distance,
several different spacings should be used. Figure 5 shows the layout
for developing the horizontal autocorrelogram on one project. It should
be emphasized that the autocorrelation coefficients at both small and
large lag distances are important, and thus a range of spacings is
necessary to adequately estimate the entire autocorrelation function and
optimize the field testing program.

Vertical Autocorrelation. Vertical autocorrelation is computed by
considering the vertical series of point values of the shear strength.
Pooling of vertical soundings can also be performed to improve the
estimate and to get a vertical autocorrelation more representative of
the entire embankment. Portions of the records that are used in pooling
must be chosen so that they are representative of the soil type that is
analyzed. Documentation of a computer program for computing vertical
autocorrelations is also presented by Anderson et al. (2).

PROBABILISTIC SLOPE STABILITY ANALYSIS AS A DESIGN TOOL

To date, probabilistic slope stability analysis has only been
applied to existing embankments. In this mode, the probabilistic
parameters must be evaluated from field and laboratory testing. When
using probabilistic slope stability analysis as a design tool, the
spatial variability of strength parameters of the in-place embankment
material cannot be measured. Therefore, it will be necessary to
establish standard autocorrelation functions and suggested values for
variances of strength parameters that can be used for design purposes.
Mean values of shear strength could be determined from conventional
laboratory testing methods. These standard autocorrelation curves and
variance values would need to be established for a variety of materials
and construction techiques.

When using probabilistic slope stability analysis in a design mode,
an important "follow up" activity is a good quality control program.
The purpose of a quality control program is to assure that the design,
including the design values of strength parameters that were used for

analysis, are achieved during construction. A conventional quality control program for embankment construction involves, among other things, measuring the dry density and moisture content of the compacted embankment material. Certain density and moisture content requirements must be met to assure that the design strength parameters are achieved. Probabilistic slope stability analysis requires not only a design value for shear strength but a characterization of the spatial variability of shear strength. The quality control program during construction must, therefore, evaluate mean and variance of shear strength and the autorcorrelation functions for each material. This can be done by making in-place density measurements during construction at specific locations along lines in the x and z directions. The autocorrelation functions in the y (vertical) direction can be established from measurements taken along vertical lines as construction proceeds. Assessment of the probability of slope failure can thereby be updated during the construction phase.

CONCLUSIONS

The probabilistic slope stability studies that have been conducted thus far at Utah State University seem to indicate that spatial variability of soil properties contributes very little to the probability of slope stability failures. In general, the spatial variability of soil properties, on the two tailings dams that have been investigated, was significantly overshadowed by model error as a contributor to probability of failure. The procedure, however, for quantifying spatial variability appears to be valid and additional case studies on other types of earth structure should be carried out.

The requirements for conducting a subsurface investigation that were briefly described in this paper clearly indicate that the effort involved for a probabilistic analysis is much greater than that required for a conventional analysis. When compared to the overall cost of earth dams and the consequences of failure, however, the additional cost seems insignificant if it will reduce the uncertainty regarding failure.

The need for developing and applying risk-based analysis to civil works is urgent. Probabilistic slope stability analysis as only one small step in developing a full risk analysis methodology and the other components of the analysis should quickly be developed.

REFERENCES

1. Alonso, E. E., "Risk Analysis of Slopes and its Application to Slopes in Canadian Sensitive Clays," Geotechnique, Vol. 26, No. 3, 1976, pp. 453-472.

2. Anderson, L. R., Bowles, D. S., Canfield, R. V., and Sharp, K. D., "Probabilistic Modeling of Tailings Embankment Designs," Contract No. J0295029, U. S. Bureau of Mines, Washington, DC, Jan., 1981, four volumes.

3. Bergado, D. T., "Probabilistic Assessment of the Safety of Earth Slopes Using Pore Water Pressure as a Random Variable," thesis

presented to Utah State University at Logan, Ut., in 1982, in partial fulfillment of the requirements for the degree of Doctor of Philosophy.

4. Bergado, D. T., and Anderson, L. R., "Stochastic Analysis of Slopes," Proceedings of the Fourth International Conference on Applications of Statistics and Probability in Soil and Structural Engineering, Florence, Italy, Vol. 2, June, 1983, pp. 1377-1388.

5. Bowles, D. S., Anderson, L. R., and Canfield, R. V., "A Systems Approach to Risk Analysis for an Earth Dan," presented at the June 1978, International Symposiumm on Risk and Reliability in Water Resources, held at Waterloo, Ontario, Canada.

6. Bowles, D. S., Anderson, L. R., Canfield, R. V., and Sharp, K. D., "Probabilistic Slope Stability Methodology," Proceedings of the Seminar on Applications of Probabilistic Methods in Geotechnical Engineering, Mary Ellen Hynes-Griffin, Editor. U. S. Army Corps of Engineers, Vicksburg, Mississippi, 1983.

7. Cornell, C. A., "First Order Uncertainty Analysis of Soils Deformation and Stability," Proceedings of the First International Conference on Applications of Statistics and Probability in Soil and Structural Engineering, Hong Kong, 1971, pp. 130-144.

8. Harr, M. E., Mechanics of Particulate Media, 1st ed., McGraw-Hill Inc., USA, 1977, 543 p.

9. Jones, G. A., and Van Zyl, D. J. A., "The Piezometer Probe--A Useful Site Investigation Tool," Presented at the 1981 Tenth International Conference on Soil Mechanics and Foundation Engineering, held at Stockholm, Sweden.

10. Mitchell, J. K., and Lunne, T. A., "Cone Resistance as Measure of Sand Strength," Journal of the Geotechnical Engineering Division, ASCE, Vol. 104, No. GT7, July, 1977, pp. 995-1012.

11. Peck, R. B., "Art and Science in Subsurface Engineering," Geotechnique Vol. 12, No. 1, 1962, p. 60.

12. Schmertmann, J. H., "Guidelines for Cone Penetration Test Performance and Design," FHWA-TS-78-209, Federal Highway Administration Office of Research and Development Implementation Division, Washington, DC, Feb., 1977.

13. Sharp, K. D., Anderson, L. R., Bowles, D. S., and Canfield, R. V., "Model for Assessing Slope Reliability," Transportation Research Record, Vol. 809, 1981, pp. 70-78.

14. Vanmarcke, E. H., "Probabilistic Modeling of Soil Profiles," Journal of the Geotechnical Engineering Division, ASCE, Vol. 103, No. GT11, 1977, pp. 1127-1246.

15. Vanmarcke, E. H., "Earth Slope Reliability," Journal of the Geotechnical Engineering Division, ASCE, Vol. 103, No. GT11, 1977, pp. 1247-1268.

16. Whitman, R. V., and Bailey, W. A., "Use of Computers for Slope Stability Analysis", Journal of Soil Mechanics and Foundations Division, ASCE, Vol. 93, No. SM4, 1967, pp. 475-498.

Characteristics of Indiana Soil Properties

Y-K T. Lo[1] and G. P. McCabe[2]

Abstract

The Indiana Geotechnical Data Bank was established to collect engineering soil data in the state and to provide information for engineering planning and design works. It contains nearly 10,000 sets of soil data.

The soil data are grouped by using physiographical regions, engineering classifications, pedological soil classifications, or a combination of these. Robust statistical methods are employed to examine the sample distributions of the data and to determine distribution parameters. Various sample comparison methods are applied to refine the grouping units. Regression analysis is used to predict design parameters from index properties, locations and parent materials.

For the engineering soil analysis in this study, robust statistical methods are preferred to conventional parametric methods. Grouping units of soil data and their distribution parameters are established. A good homogeneity of soil characteristics is obtained with these groupings. The equations developed to predict soil design parameters from index properties are reasonably accurate. Finally, practical uses of this data bank for typical highway projects are suggested.

Introduction

The computerized Indiana Geotechnical Data Bank was established to collect pedologic and engineering soil information from private consulting firms, soil testing laboratories and from tests conducted by Indiana Department of Transportation. A data storage and retrieval system is used to generate information for building highways, bridges and other facilities in the state.

The methodology used in forming this bank and its development are discussed in the reports by Goldberg (1) and Lo (4). In addition, the nature and some uses of the Bank are described in papers by Goldberg, et al (2) and Lo and Lovell (5). The Bank is user oriented and flexible in the sense that both data in the same categories and data from other categories can be added as needed.

---

[1] Geotechnical Engineer, Woodward-Clyde Consultants, 202 North Golden Circle Drive, Santa Ana, CA 92705

[2] Professor of Statistics, Department of Statistics, Purdue University, West Lafayette, Ind. 47907

For a typical highway subsurface investigation, data generally is taken at limited depths and only soil classification tests are involved. Bridge locations receive more detailed attention. In general the geotechnical data are widely scattered in area and limited to simple index properties.

Visual textural classification and color in a moist condition are available for all samples. If the sample is to be classified according to the Unified System or the AASHO System, grain size distribution and or Atterberg limits are required as well.

Other variables in the data bank include
        organic content,
        natural water content,
        in-place densities (wet or dry),
        specific gravity,
        compaction curves,
        California bearing ratio (CBR) for compacted and soaked soils,
        unconfined undrained strength and other strength parameters,
        compressibility parameters,
        standard penetration test (SPT) values particularly for sand,
        depth to the water table and depth to bedrock, if encountered,
        boring location - township, range and section.

Pedologic maps are used to identify the soil association and the series. The usual generalized ratings (available for pedologically classified soils) are assigned to samples as appropriate. These ratings include: erosion class, natural drainage class, permeability, flooding potential, frost heave susceptibility, shrink-swell potential, and pH. It is also possible to access the regional geomorphic (physiographic) location of boring, and to group data according to these units.

Data can be retrieved for analysis by any description of location, depth or type. They may be simply printed out and examined qualitatively, or subjected to statistical analysis.

Descriptive Statistical Analysis

To describe the variability of selected soil characteristics, the frequency distributions of these characteristics are examined. Robust estimates, such as median, confidence interval of median, percentiles, and interquartile range (7) are used to describe the sample distributions in this study. The sample distributions found were frequently non-normal. Medians were used to characterize center of the sample distribution. If the distribution is symmetric, the mean and the median coincide. With highly skewed distributions the median is preferred, since it seems to represent the concept of a center better than the mean. The interquartile range (IR), defined as the difference between the 75th and the 25th percentiles, is used as a measure of population variability rather than standard deviation.

The following characteristics were described using these measures:

    (1) Topographic characteristics:

The topographic characteristics are examined within physiographic regions. Table 1 shows the distribution of ground
water elevation for the total state and for some of the 13 physiographic regions within the state.
(2) Relationships between the remolded soil characteristics and
AASHTO classification within a physiographic region:

To develop these kinds of relationships on a regional basis,
the following procedures are used.

  (a) Examine the distribution of AASHTO classification units
      within a given physiographic region and select three or
      four most probable AASHTO classification units as the
      representative soil groups in the region.
  (b) Examine the distributions of both visual texture and Uni-
      fied classification units for each of the selected AASHTO
      classification units within the specific region. Select
      the most probable texture and Unified classification
      units as the representatives for soil identification and
      correlation.
  (c) Apply appropriate statistical methods to obtain the esti-
      mates for sample distributions of the following remolded
      soil characteristics: natural dry density, (NATDD),
      specific gravity (SPECGR), shrinkage limit (SL), maximum
      dry density (MAXDD), optimum moisture content (OMC), CBR
      value at 100% maximum dry density (CBR SO1), and CBR value
      at 95% maximum dry density (CBR SO2) for each classifica-
      tion unit selected above. A typical result is illus-
      trated in Table 2.

(3) Statistical soil profiles

The statistical soil profiles were generated according to the
pedological soil associations, because these are the only soil
grouping units which are reasonably large and grossly homogeneous.
The following is an outline of the procedures used to generate a
statistical soil profile for a given soil association. More detail
is given in Lo (4).

  (a) Examine the counties and physiographic regions with the
      given soil association and select representative
      locations.

  (b) Apply appropriate statistical methods to assess the dis-
      tributional parameters of topographic characteristics at
      the given locations.

  (c) Establish the soil profile by examining the distributions
      of the AASHTO classification units within the given soil
      association and select the ones with highest frequencies
      as representatives.

  (d) Use 90th percentiles of top and bottom depths from which
      the sample has been removed as upper and lower depth

Table 1. Ground water level with respect to ground level (ft)

Physiographic region	Mean	s.d.	Median	95% C.I. of median	t.25*	t.75**	I.R.***	Minimum	Maximum
Whole state (2395 cases)	5.40	4.80	4.33	4.13--4.53	2.11	6.73	4.62	0.10	60.00
Tipton Till Plain (834 cases)	5.16	3.41	4.10	3.86--4.37	2.50	6.12	3.62	0.20	20.00
Dearborn Upland (89 cases)	4.93	2.96	4.21	3.54--4.86	2.54	5.86	3.32	0.50	15.00
Norman Upland (83 cases)	7.67	5.52	6.54	5.78--7.23	4.44	8.50	4.06	0.50	17.00
Mitchell Plain (140 cases)	8.54	7.22	6.29	5.61--7.03	4.33	8.84	4.51	1.00	38.00
Crawford Upland (144 cases)	8.77	8.01	6.45	5.70--7.18	4.07	10.00	5.93	0.50	60.00
Wabash Lowland (348 cases)	5.88	5.38	4.12	3.75--4.61	2.54	7.06	4.52	0.10	37.00
Calumet Lacustrine Section (204 cases)	5.84	5.63	4.08	3.45--4.82	1.89	8.07	6.18	0.20	35.00
Valparaiso Moraine (150 cases)	2.26	1.72	1.86	1.55--2.28	0.94	3.31	2.37	0.10	10.00
Steuben Morainal Section (335 cases)	3.98	3.81	2.96	2.59--3.33	1.39	4.92	3.53	0.10	35.00

*25% quartile   **75% quartile   ***Interquartile Range

Table 2. Characteristics of soil properties obtained from disturbed soil testing within Tipton Till Plain

Physiographic region: Tipton Till Plain
AASHTO classification: A-4
Texture: sandy loam, clay loam
Unified classification: CL, CL-ML

Variable	Mean	s.d.	Median	t.25	t.75	I.R.	95% C.I. of median	Minimum	Maximum	No. of Cases
NATDD	104.33	21.51	106.17	94.14	120.75	26.61	100.57--111.17	12.40	132.00	41
SPECGR	2.70	0.046	2.69	2.66	2.73	0.07	2.66--2.73	2.64	2.77	13
SL	14.05	3.28	13.23	11.21	15.65	4.44	12.89--13.57	0.10	26.00	552
MAXDD	120.53	7.12	122.26	115.76	126.29	10.53	120.00--124.52	98.20	130.70	49
OMC	12.27	3.04	11.25	10.00	13.43	3.43	10.55--15.95	8.30	24.70	48
CBRS01	10.38	6.61	8.20	6.30	12.50	6.20	7.00--10.00	3.00	42.10	37
CBRS02	6.07	2.70	5.00	3.33	7.67	4.34	3.87--6.33	2.00	14.00	39

boundaries of the soil profile for each selected AASHTO classification unit within the given soil association. This was done to eliminate the extremes of depths from which the sample has been removed and, hopefully, to minimize the discontinuity of soil sample versus depth distributions.

(e) Divide the soil profile into sublayers based on the further examinations of the distributions of selected AASHTO classification units versus depths.

(f) Apply appropriate statistical methods to obtain the estimates of characteristics of engineering soils at each sublayer.

Table 3 shows the statistical soil profile for association Fincastle - Ragsdale - Brookston at the physiographic region of Tipton Till Plain.

Regression Analyses

Regression analyses provide a convenient method for investigating relationships among variables. In this study design parameters, such as compaction and compressibility characteristics, are correlated with soil index properties. The effects of soil location and genesis - i.e. physiographic region and parent material are incorporated into the regression equations using dummy variables (6).

The variables are selected to minimize the mean square due to error of the prediction. Because a large value of R^2 (square of multiple) correlation coefficient) or a significant t-statistic does not ensure that the data are well fit, a careful residual analysis is also made. The procedure used to reduce the number of independent variables is to compare the full model and the reduced model with an F-statistic (6).

The regression analysis is discussed in detail and reported by Lo (4,5) and is not further considered here.

Discussion of Results

The descriptive statistics and regression analyses are developed to provide information for future planning. Such information is useful if it provides an accurate picture of what can be expected. Small confidence intervals for the median, small interquartile ranges and large values of the squared multiple correlation coefficient (R^2) are associated with good descriptions and regression analyses. In cases where such results are not obtained, either more data or a different grouping procedure is needed.

The Medians and Soil Variability

In this study soils were grouped by physiographic regions, AASHTO classifications, soil associations, or a combination of these. The sample distributions of soil characteristics were studied according to these groups. The median of the sample distribution of a soil

Table 3   Typical soil profile for soil association.

Fincastle-Ragsdale-Brookston

General description: Nearly level, somewhat poorly drained, silty Fincastle in windblown silt and glacial till, very poorly drained, silty Ragsdale in windblown silts and loamy Brookston in glacial till.

Parent material: Soils formed in moderately thick loess deposits over loamy Wisconsin age glacial till.

Distributions: Physiographic region: Tipton Till Plain
Counties: Tippecanoe, little in Clinton

Ground elevation:

Mean	s.d.	Median	t.25	t.75	I.R.	95% C.I. of Median	Minimum	Maximum	N. of Cases
728.12	70.26	708.33	673.81	788.88	115.07	685.71-761.11	645.90	866.80	47

Ground water level:

Season	Mean	s.d.	Median	t.25	t.75	I.R.	95% C.I. of Median	Minimum	Maximum	N. of Cases
Total	723.17	69.76	708.33	672.50	785.00	112.50	685.00-700.00	641.70	854.90	47
Winter	846.68	13.85	875.00	850.00	883.33	33.33		826.10	854.90	4
Spring	759.11	62.15	725.00	695.00	806.25	111.25	700.00-800.00	662.60	808.90	17
Summer	653.26	7.16	671.43	653.57	689.29	35.72	650.00-663.00	641.70	663.50	9
Fall	695.18	36.03	700.00	671.87	737.50	65.63	675.00-733.33	642.50	767.30	17

Ground water level with respect to ground level:

Season	Mean	s.d.	Median	t.25	t.75	I.R.	95% C.I. of Median	Minimum	Maximum	N. of Cases
Total	4.95	2.67	4.00	2.91	6.00	3.09	3.36-5.17	1.60	11.90	47
Winter	9.53	4.36	11.00	4.00	11.33	7.33	10.00-11.90	3.00	11.91	4
Spring	3.33	1.38	3.17	2.42	3.92	1.50	2.50-3.83	1.60	6.00	17
Summer	4.42	0.87	4.86	4.14	5.57	1.43	4.00-5.40	3.00	5.40	9
Fall	5.78	2.40	6.00	3.28	7.28	4.00	3.43-7.14	2.50	10.00	17

Table 3 (continued). Typical soil profile.

Unified classification: CL   Texture: clay and silty loam
PH. 5.10 - 6.00   Organic material: not traceable

Unified classification: CL, CH   Texture: clay, silty clay and silty clay loam
PH: 5.60 - 6.00   Organic material: not traceable

Variable	Mean	s.d.	Median	t.25	t.75	I.R.	Min.	Max.	No. of Cases
SPT	5		5						1
SL	15.82	4.18	15.16	12.88	17.89	5.01	2.00	29.00	102
NATMC	23.00	8.11	22.50	17.78	27.67	9.89	8.00	65.00	67
NATDD	93.37	6.50	92.40	85.00	97.50	12.50	84.60	98.40	4
SPECGR	2.72	0.03	2.72	2.70	2.75	0.05	2.67	2.77	6
MAXDD	105.18	13.23	104.00	100.50	117.50	17.00	80.00	125.00	13
OMC	21.65	13.42	20.00	15.50	24.50	9.00	10.00	63.00	13
CBRS01	7.86	2.14	7.67	6.50	10.33	3.83	4.50	11.30	13
CBRO2	4.71	1.68	4.67	3.25	5.83	2.58	2.00	9.00	13
QU	1.43	0.49	1.20				1.10	2.00	3

Depth in Feet profile: A-7-6, A-6, A-4 (0 to 4)

Table 3 (continued).

Unified classification: CL   Texture: clay, silty clay loam, and sandy loam
PH: 7.40 - 7.80   Organic material: not traceable

Variable	Mean	s.d.	Median	t.25	t.75	I.R.	Min.	Max.	No. of Cases
SPT	63	23	63				47	80	2
SL	13.69	3.35	13.50	10.13	16.50	6.37	9.00	18.00	13
NATMC	17.82	6.49	18.12	12.50	25.00	12.50	10.00	27.00	12
NATDD	103.00	2.48	103.33	100.83	105.00	4.17	99.80	106.20	5
SPECGR	2.76	.021	2.76				2.74	2.77	2
MAXDD	128.45	0.50	128.45				128.10	128.80	2
OMC	10.20	0.14	10.20				10.10	10.30	2
CBRS01	9.50	2.12	9.50				8.00	11.00	2
CBRS02	5.50	0.71	5.50				5.00	6.00	2
Qu	0.70	0.28	0.70				0.50	0.90	2

Note:

SPT-Standard penetration resistance
NATMC-Natural moisture content(%)
SPECGR-Specific gravity
OMC-Optimum moisture content (%)
Qu-Unconfined compressive strength (TSF)

SL-Shrinkage Limit(%)
NATDD-Natural dry density (PCF)
MAXDD-Maximum dry density (PCF)
CBRS01-CBR soaked value at 100% maximum dry density
CBRS02-CBR soaked value at 95% maximum dry density

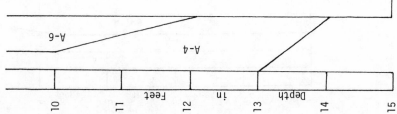

Table 3 (continued).

Unified classification: CL, CL-ML   Texture: clay loam and sandy loam

PH: 6.10 - 6.50   Organic material: not traceable

Variable	Mean	s.d.	Median	t.25	t.75	I.R.	Min.	Max.	No. of Cases
SPT	7	4	7				5	10	2
SL	13.38	3.32	13	13.00	10.90	4.02	1.90	24.00	45
NATMC	21.50	11.12	18.54	15.00	23.57	8.57	11.00	65.00	34
NATDD	86.13	7.03	85.30	80.00	90.00	10.00	77.60	93.50	4
SPECGR	2.72	0.007	2.72				2.71	2.72	2
MAXDD	125.65	0.50	125.65				125.30	126.00	2
OMC	10.25	0.35	10.25				10.00	10.50	2
CBRS01	6.60		6.60						1
CBRS02	3.90		3.90						1
Qu	0.67	0.115	0.65				0.60	0.80	3

characteristic was used as the central measure.

Since medians rather than means are used, the usual analysis of variance procedures for testing equality of groups are inapplicable. However, nonparametric versions of these methods are available (3) and are used extensively in this study.

Topographic Characteristics Versus Physiographic Regions

Topographic characteristics are grouped according to physiographic regions. The test results verify that the topographic features, such as the ground elevations and ground water elevations vary with physiographic regions (4). In addition, the elevation and ruggedness varies with physiographic region.

Remolded Soil Characteristics Versus Physiographic Regions and AASHTO Classifications

The sample distributions of remolded soil characteristics were studied according to AASHTO classifications for each physiographic region. This is a two-way classification, i.e., the grouping effects are due to a combination of AASHTO classifications and physiographic regions. Results indicate that the remolded soil characteristics vary with both grouping units (4). These analyses also verify the facts that the more plastic soils have lower maximum dry density and higher optimum moisture content values (4).

Soil Characteristics Versus Soil Associations

The layout for the generation or a statistical soil profile involves a breakdown of the data for each soil characteristic by physiographic regions, and then by soil associations. Finally they are grouped into proper layer systems. Results indicate that only some of the soil characteristics vary with soil associations (4). Large variability among soil association units is found in this study (4). This may mean either that: (1) the soil samples are not sufficient for verification, or (2) the grouping unit is not refined sufficiently. In the latter case a subgrouping unit such as soil series may be useful. This subject needs further research.

Soil Series as a Grouping Unit

The results of the multiple comparison tests of soil characteristics versus soil series indicate that the soil characteristics do not vary significantly with soil series (4). Therefore, the soil series as a grouping unit is indicated to be inferior to the soil association. However, wide scatter of the data and relatively small sample sizes of soil characteristics are present. Further study is required to investigate this point in detail.

Applications

The uses of Indiana Geotechnical Data Bank for typical highway projects are described in the report by Lo (4). These examples show the uses of this data base (1) to determine the soil types and topography within a specific area and the engineering characteristics of these soils, (2) to develop a more efficient and economical subsurface exploration program, (3) to test the consistency and reliability of laboratory testing results, and (4) to make recommendations for design and construction of proposed highways and their relevant facilities.

Summary

A computerized data storage and retrieval system has been developed for the State of Indiana. Both conventional and nonparametric statistical methods are employed in the analysis of these data. The studies on the topographic characteristics versus physiographic region were based on a one-way classification. The results give a general impression of the topographic features of a physiographic region and can be used to make comparisons of overall topographic features among regions. The methods can also be applied to smaller areas if topographic data are adequate. The studies on the remolded soil characteristics versus physiographic regions and AASHTO classifications are based on a two-way classification, and show the relationships on a regional basis. The studies on statistical soil profiles show the general subsoil conditions qualitatively and provide estimates of soil characteristics quantitatively by depth for soil associations on a regional basis. Finally, the regression analysis gives good to adequate relations between design parameters and index properties.

Conclusions

1. Topographic features vary with physiographic regions.

2. The remolded soil characteristics can be evaluated and contrasted among physiographic regions and also among AASHTO classifications.

3. The data confirm that the more plastic soils have lower maximum dry density and higher optimum moisture content values.

4. The soil association is the most refined unit presently available for grouping soils to generate soil profiles.

5. Nonparametric robust statistical methods are preferred to conventional statistical methods for soil data analysis.

6. The physiographic region, engineering soil classification, soil association, and a combination of these are used as grouping units. The interquartile ranges (IR's) for most soil characteristics are small and tolerable. In other words, a good homogeneity of soil characteristics is evidenced with these groupings.

7. The data bank is valuable for making recommendations for preliminary design of geotechnical works. It can also be used as a framework against which various testing results can be judged for their consistency and reliability.

ACKNOWLEDGEMENT

    The research described in this paper was carried out under the sponsorship of the Joint Highway Research Project of Purdue University, the Indiana State Highway Commission, and the Federal Highway Administration. Their support is gratefully acknowledged. We thank C. W. Lovell for his guidence throughout the project; R. D. Miles for his assistance, including valuable editorial aid; and T. R. West for valuable geological advice.

References

1. Goldberg, G. D. (1978) Development of the Computerized Geotechnical Data Bank for the State of Indiana. Purdue University, West Lafayette, IN, M.S.C.E. thesis and Joint Highway Research Project Report No. 76-6.

2. Goldberg, G. D., Lovell, C. W. and Miles, R. D. (1978) Use the Geotechnical Data Bank. TRB, Transportation Research Record 702, 140-146.

3. Hollander, M. and Wolfe, D. A. (1973) Nonparametric Statistical Methods. Wiley, New York.

4. Lo, Y-K. T. (1980) Geotechnical Data Bank for Indiana. Purdue University, West Lafayette, IN, Ph.D. thesis and Joing Highway Research Project Report No. 80-7.

5. Lo, Y-K. T. and Lovell, C. W. (1982) Prediction of Soil Properties from Simple Indices. TRB, Transportation Research Record 873, 43-49.

6. Neter, J. and Wasserman, W. (1974) Applied Linear Statistical Models, Irwin, Homewood, Illinois.

7. Tukey, J. W. (1977) Exploring Data Analysis, Addison-Wesley, Reading, Massachusetts.

COEFFICIENT OF VARIATION OF IN SITU TESTS IN SAND

Jean-Louis Briaud[1] and Larry Tucker[1]

Abstract

For a research project on the behavior of piles in sand for the United States Geological Survey and the Federal Highway Administration, ten sites were selected where detailed load tests had been performed on instrumented piles. The soil data at each site was collected and consisted mainly of in situ tests including Standard Penetration Tests, Cone Penetrometer Tests, Pressuremeter Tests, Cross Hole Shear Wave Velocity Tests.

The standard deviation, mean and coefficient of variation were calculated for each in situ test results. The results show that the coefficient of variation in the vertical direction is equal to approximately 1.5 times the one in the horizontal direction, that the coefficient of variation for the SPT, CPT and PMT results are similar, while it is much lower for the cross hole test. Applications of the results to the precision of ultimate pile capacity predictions is discussed at the end of the paper. It is shown that the variation in soil data explains 36% of the error in the predicted ultimate pile capacity.

Introduction

For a research project on the behavior of piles in sand for the Federal Highway Administration and the United States Geological Survey, ten sites were selected where detailed load tests had been performed on instrumented piles (1). The soil data at each site was collected and consisted mainly of in situ tests including Standard Penetration Tests (SPT), Cone Penetrometer Tests (CPT), Pressuremeter tests (PMT), Cross Hole Shear Wave Velocity Tests (SWVT) (12).

Because the variability of soil properties across a site is a major factor influencing the accuracy of pile capacity predictions, a statistical analysis of the available soil data was performed. The two terms used to characterize the data are the mean, μ, and the standard deviation, σ. They are defined as

$$\mu = \frac{\sum\limits_{i=1}^{n} (X_i)}{n} \quad \cdots\cdots\cdots\cdots\cdots\cdots\cdots\cdots \quad (1)$$

and

$$\sigma = \frac{\sum\limits_{i=1}^{n} (X_i-\mu)^2}{n - 1} \quad \cdots\cdots\cdots\cdots\cdots\cdots\cdots \quad (2)$$

---

1. Associate Professor, Research Assistant, Civil Engineering Department, Texas A&M University, College Station, TX 77843.

where X is the data to be analyzed and n is the total number of data points entered. The ratio of the standard deviation over the mean is the coefficient of variation. This coefficient gives an indication of the scatter in the data. Applications of the results to the precision of ultimate pile capacity predictions is discussed at the end of the paper. It is shown that the variation in soil data explains 36% of the error in the predicted ultimate pile capacity.

Data Base

The pile load tests and the corresponding soil tests available at each site are shown on Table 1. As can be seen from that table the most common test at those sites was the SPT, then came the CPT followed by the PMT and the SWVT. The sands varied from very loose to very dense and from very fine to very coarse.

Standard Penetration Test (SPT)

The standard penetration test was performed at eight of the ten sites considered. At one of these sites, the Corpus Christi site, the Texas Highway Department dynamic penetration test was performed and the results were converted to SPT N values. Examples of SPT profiles are presented in Figs. 1 and 2.

Vertical Analysis

First, a vertical analysis was performed (12). This analysis consisted of taking the mean and standard deviation of the blow count values for each boring separately. Then all the borings at one site were analyzed together to determine the variation across the entire site. The coefficient of variation at each site ranged from 0.164 to 1.148 with an average for all the sites of 0.707.

Horizontal Analysis

Due to a lack of data at some sites, a horizontal analysis could be performed at only four sites. This analysis was performed by taking all the blow count values within a certain layer across the site and computing the mean and standard deviation for that layer, Fig.1 (12). The coefficient of variation at each site varied from 0.144 to 0.770 with an average for all sites of 0.421.

Two horizontal analyses were performed at the Lock and Dam 26 Ellis Island site. One used 20 borings along a line approximately 3000 feet (914 m) long parallel to the axis of the river. The other used 13 borings in an area 400 feet by 200 feet (122 m x 61 m). The results show (Table 2) that the coefficient of variation increases with the area considered and with the testing depth.

The coeficient of variation of the SPT data in the horizontal direction is equal to 0.59 times the coefficient of variation in the

TABLE 1.- Sites and Soil Data Available

Site (1)	Piles (2)	SPT (3)	CPT (4)	PMT (5)	Other (6)	Reference (7)
Lock & Dam 4, Arkansas River (1963)	Steel Pipe Steel H	X				3,6
Low Sill Structure Old River, La. (1956)	Steel Pipe Steel H	X				7
Ogeechee River	Steel Pipe	X	X		Density	13,14
Lock & Dam 26, Replacement Site (1972)	Steel H	X				4
West Seattle Freeway Bridge (1980)	Octogonal Concrete	X			Self- boring PMT	9,10
Tavenas (1970)	Steel H Hexagonal Concrete	X	X			.11
Gregersen (1969)	Circular Concrete	X	X			5
Corpus Christi (1971)	Square Concrete				Texas Highway Cone	2
Sellgren (1981)	Square Concrete			X		8
Lock & Dam 26 Ellis Island (1978)	Timber	X	X	X	Shear Wave Velocity	15,16

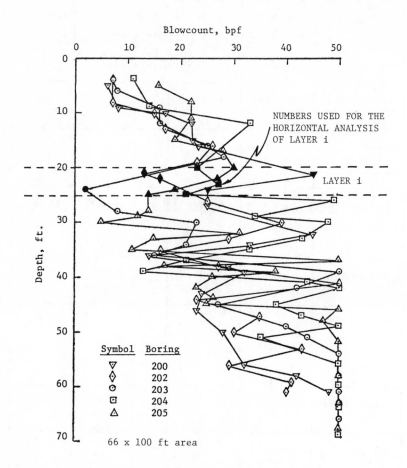

FIG. 1.- Lock and Dam 4, Arkansas River: SPT
Data (1ft = 0.3048 m)

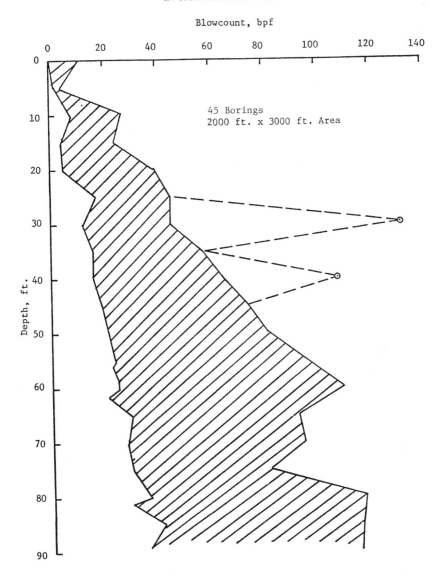

FIG. 2 .- Lock and Dam 26, New Dam Site: SPT Data
        (1 ft. = 0.3048 m)

TABLE 2.- Horizontal Analysis of SPT Data

SITE	DEPTH ft.	MEAN bpf	STD.DEV. bpf	$\frac{\sigma}{\mu}$
Lock and Dam 26, New Dam Site, 400 ft. x 200 ft. Area	0-15	57.33	35.80	0.624
	15-20	14.70	5.23	0.356
	20-25	13.83	4.62	0.335
	25-30	17.31	3.20	0.185
	30-35	19.54	6.20	0.317
	35-40	21.15	5.97	0.274
	40-45	26.57	7.73	0.291
	45-50	28.85	6.88	0.238
	50-55	33.60	14.78	0.440
	55-60	27.33	10.20	0.373
	60-65	36.15	16.08	0.445
	65-70	44.82	20.92	0.467
	70-75	48.14	18.72	0.389
	75-80	63.17	22.42	0.355
	80-90	74.13	40.92	0.552
			Avg. =	0.376
Lock and Dam 26, New Dam Site, 3000 ft. line along river axis	0- 5	-	-	-
	5-10	43.50	39.80	0.915
	10-15	14.10	5.74	0.407
	15-20	14.00	4.15	0.296
	20-25	22.40	11.65	0.520
	25-30	27.00	25.86	0.958
	30-35	25.00	11.51	0.460
	35-40	36.57	21.33	0.583
	40-45	33.35	17.03	0.511
	45-50	40.86	17.94	0.439
	50-55	44.39	24.94	0.562
	55-60	33.72	12.52	0.371
	60-65	48.16	21.37	0.444
	65-70	52.00	21.11	0.406
	70-75	42.76	16.46	0.385
	75-80	51.50	28.05	0.545
	80-85	64.70	33.30	0.515
	85-90	56.14	34.47	0.614
			Avg. =	0.525

vertical direction. This is to be expected since sand is normally deposited in layers and generally increases in strength with depth.

Influence of Number of Borings

At the site of the new Lock and Dam 26 on the Mississippi River there were about 400 borings available, spread over a very large area. An area 400 feet by 200 feet (122 m x 61 m) was chosen, in which there were 13 SPT borings done with a 3-inch sampler. An analysis was performed to determine the influence of the number of borings on the mean and standard deviation. Borings were selected from the 13 borings in a random fashion and the mean and standard deviation were computed (12). Fig. 3 shows that the mean value becomes almost constant after six borings. Fig. 4 shows that the scatter in the data steadily decreases after two borings. This analysis is definitely not general in application but does point out that there is a certain number of borings after which it is not cost effective to perform more SPT tests. This number may, however, be site specific and may thus only be obtained through experience in that locality.

Pressuremeter Tests (PMT)

Pressuremeter test results were available at three of the ten sites. The pressuremeter data at the West Seattle Freeway site however, was insufficient for use in this study. The pressuremeter test yields two main properties of the soil: the limit pressure, p_l, and a modulus of elasticity, E_{PMT}. Example profiles are presented in Fig. 5.

Vertical Analysis

The vertical analysis was done in a similar manner to that of the SPT data. The results are shown in Table 3. The range in the coefficient of variation of p_l is from 0.261 to 0.575 with an average of 0.503 for all the borings. For E_{PMT} the coefficient of variation ranges from 0.516 to 0.783 times the mean with an average of 0.619 for all the borings. The scatter in the modulus obtained from the pressuremeter is higher than that of the limit pressure. The modulus is used in the calculation of settlement, whereas the limit pressure is used in computing the pile capacity.

Horizontal Analysis

A horizontal analysis was possible only at the Lock and Dam 26 Ellis Island site. The results are shown in Table 4. As with the SPT, the pressuremeter data shows less scatter in the horizontal direction than in the vertical. The range in the coefficient of variation for p_l is from 0.225 to 0.499 with an average of 0.399. The range for E_{PMT} is from 0.282 to 0.682 with an average of 0.416. The data is too limited to support any general conclusions. It is of interest, however, to note that the average scatter of the PMT data and that of the SPT data is approximately the same. Also, for comparison, the PMT data and the SPT data for the Lock and Dam 26

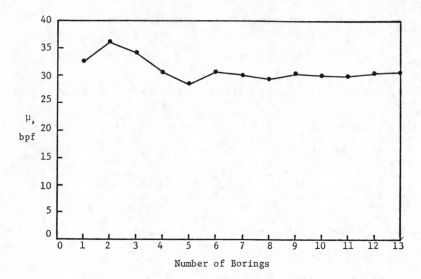

FIG. 3 – Mean of SPT Values vs. Number of Borings
(1ft. = 0.3048 m)

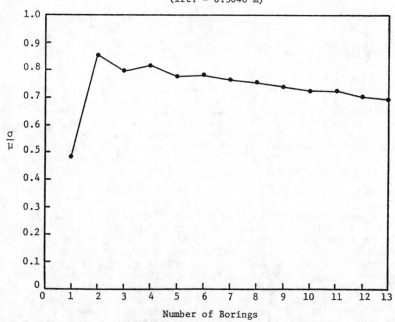

FIG. 4 – Ratio of Standard Deviation to Mean for
SPT Values vs. Number of Borings

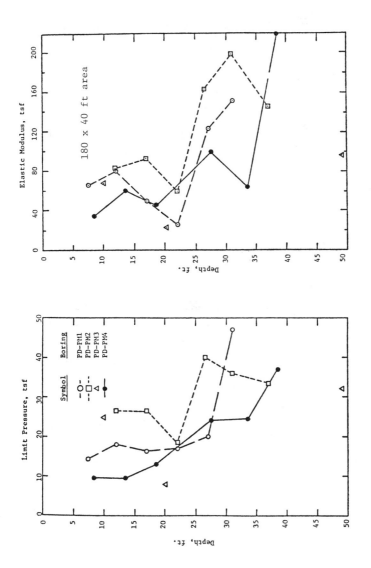

FIG. 5.— Lock and Dam 26 Ellis Island Site: PMT Data (from ref.(15)
(1 ft = 0.3048 m; 1 tsf = 95.76 kPa)

TABLE 3.- Vertical Analysis of PMT Data
(1 tsf = 95.76 kPa)

SITE	BORING	LIMIT PRESSURE			MODULUS		
		MEAN tsf	STD.DEV. tsf	$\frac{\sigma}{\mu}$	MEAN tsf	STD.DEV. tsf	$\frac{\sigma}{\mu}$
Lock and Dam 26,	PD-PM1	22.08	12.36	0.560	82.42	46.99	0.570
Ellis Island	PD-PM2	30.15	7.87	0.261	112.00	57.81	0.516
	PD-PM3	21.83	12.55	0.575	62.72	38.00	0.606
	PD-PM4	19.58	10.90	0.556	87.08	68.22	0.783
	All	23.64	10.86	0.460	90.34	54.88	0.607
Sellgren		89.60	50.40	0.562	14.20	8.78	0.619

TABLE 4.- Horizontal Analysis of PMT Data
(1 tsf = 95.76 kPa)

SITE	DEPTH ft	LIMIT PRESSURE			MODULUS		
		MEAN tsf	STD.DEV. tsf	$\frac{\sigma}{\mu}$	MEAN tsf	STD.DEV. tsf	$\frac{\sigma}{\mu}$
Lock and Dam 26,	0-10	16.17	7.97	0.493	52.43	16.15	0.315
Ellis Island	10-20	18.27	6.88	0.377	68.00	19.20	0.282
Site	20-30	21.25	10.60	0.499	82.53	52.29	0.682
	30-40	35.66	8.04	0.225	155.66	59.73	0.384
			Avg. =	0.399		Avg. =	0.416

Ellis Island site were obtained in the same borehole and the scatter in the data is comparable in both the horizontal and vertical directions.

Cross-Hole Shear Wave Velocity

Cross-hole shear wave velocity test data was also available at the Lock and Dam 26 Ellis Island site (Fig. 6). The results of the vertical analysis are presented in Table 5, the horizontal analysis in Table 6. The soil shear modulus, G, is related to the shear wave velocity, V_s, by:

$$G = \frac{\gamma_t}{g} V_s^2 \quad \ldots \ldots \ldots \ldots \ldots \ldots \ldots \ldots \quad (3)$$

where γ_t is the total unit weight of the soil and g is the gravitational acceleration. Using the second order approximation of the Taylor series expansion for expected values, the coefficient of variation, $\frac{\sigma}{\mu}$, for G is:

$$(\frac{\sigma}{\mu})G = \frac{2(\frac{\sigma}{\mu})_{V_s}}{1 + (\frac{\sigma}{\mu})^2_{V_s}} \quad \ldots \ldots \ldots \ldots \ldots \ldots \ldots \ldots \quad (4)$$

The average coefficient of variation for G is therefore 0.327 in the vertical direction and 0.259 in the horizontal direction. This represents a scatter in the data which is 40 percent less than the SPT and PMT data at this site.

Soil Density

The total and dry densities of the soil were measured at three of the ten sites. At the Arkansas River and Gregersen sites the measurements were made in the laboratory on samples. These measurements may therefore be influenced by disturbances due to sampling. The measurements at the Ogeechee River site were made in situ with a nuclear probe, and may be less affected by disturbance. An example of density profile is shown in Fig. 7 and the results of the analysis are given in Table 7. Only a vertical analysis was performed due to the small quantity of data at each site. The coefficient of variation is much smaller, averaging 0.057, than that of the other tests analyzed. However, the strength of the soil is much more sensitive to changes in the density than changes in the other parameters.

Static Cone Penetration Test (CPT)

Static cone penetration tests results were available at five sites. An example of the data is shown in Fig. 8. No analysis of this data was performed due to the continuous nature of the readings.

TABLE 7.- Analysis of Total and Dry Density
(1 lb/ft^3 = 16.02 kg/m^3)

SITE	BORING		MEAN lb/ft^3	STD.DEV lb/ft^3	$\frac{\sigma}{\mu}$
Lock and Dam 4, Arkansas River	201	γ_d	103.40	7.40	0.072
Gregersen		γ_t	121.60	4.51	0.037
		γ_d	90.81	14.08	0.155
Ogeechee River	N1	γ_t	125.58	4.55	0.036
		γ_d	102.50	3.86	0.038
	N2	γ_t	125.75	6.63	0.053
		γ_d	103.61	3.83	0.037
	N3	γ_t	125.61	5.77	0.046
		γ_d	103.33	3.92	0.038

Note: γ_d = dry density
γ_t = total density

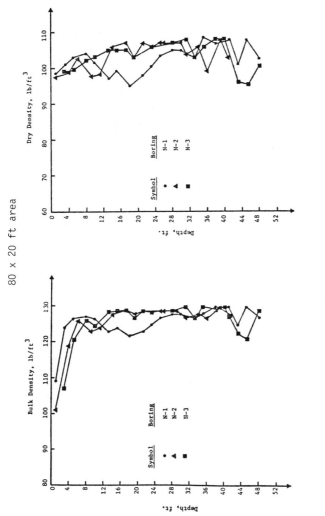

FIG. 7.— Ogeechee River Site: Bulk and Dry Density
(1ft. = 0.3048m; 1 lb/ft³ = 16.02 kg/m³)

TABLE 5.- Vertical Analysis of Cross-hole Shear Wave Data
(1 ft/sec = 30.48 cm/sec)

SITE	BORING	MEAN ft/sec	STD.DEV. ft/sec	$\frac{\sigma}{\mu}$
Lock and Dam 26, Ellis Island Site	PD-S6,S7	607.3	105.2	0.173
	PD-S9,S10	675.1	103.9	0.154
	PD-S1,S2	582.2	98.7	0.170
	PD-S4,S5	580.7	102.1	0.176
	All	607.0	105.4	0.174
			Avg. =	0.168

TABLE 6.- Horizontal Analysis of Cross-hole Shear Wave Data

SITE	DEPTH ft	MEAN ft/sec	STD.DEV. ft/sec	$\frac{\sigma}{\mu}$
Lock and Dam 26, Ellis Island Site	5	472.0	22.1	0.047
	10	514.5	44.4	0.086
	15	606.3	92.7	0.153
	20	554.2	88.6	0.160
	25	640.6	132.5	0.207
	30	603.0	78.0	0.129
	35	684.6	82.6	0.121
	40	681.0	136.5	0.200
	45	664.5	54.5	0.082
			Avg. =	0.132

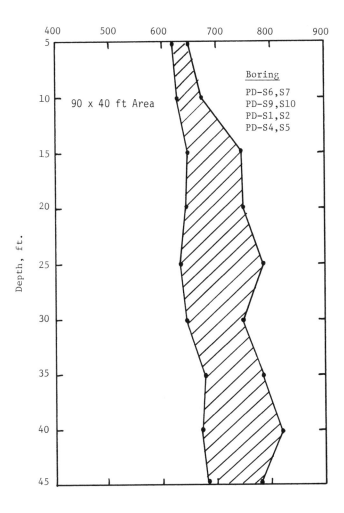

FIG 6.- Lock and Dam 26, Ellis Island Site: Crosshole
        Shear Wave Data (from ref. 15) (1 ft. = 0.3048;
        1 ft/sec = 30.48 cm/sec.)

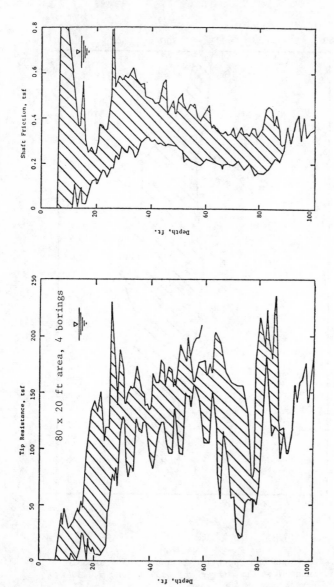

FIG. 8.-- Ogeechee River Site: CPT Data (from ref. 13)(1 tsf = 95.76; 1 ft. = 0.3048 m)

However, a comparison of the range of CPT results to that of the SPT and PMT results shows generally the same scatter for all three type of tests.

Discussion

The coefficients of variation for the various soil tests discussed are summarized in Table 8. This table is somewhat misleading. The coefficient of variation is low for the density measurements but soil parameters are very sensitive to changes in density. The pressuremeter test and the cone penetrometer tests do not show a coefficient of variation significantly lower than the Standard Penetration Test. However, the repeatability of the SPT test from one crew to another and from one type of hammer to another has not been considered in this statistical analysis. Indeed the coefficients of variation were calculated at each site where the same crew and hammer were involved. There is little doubt that if repeatability was included the cone penetrometer would come first. The small strain shear moduli obtained from shear wave velocity tests show a smaller scatter than other parameters.

Another consideration is to evaluate the degree of dependency between the ultimate capacity of the pile and the soil parameter measured. In this respect the fact that the SWVT provides less scatter is of little help to the engineer. Yet another point to consider is the unit cost of each test.

Precision of Pile Capacity Prediction Methods

In the process of predicting the ultimate capacity of a pile, a number of errors occur. These are: 1. The error due to the natural variability of the soil; this is tied to the fact that the pile load test and the soil test are not performed at the same location. 2. The error in testing of the soil; this is for example the error on the N value associated with the Standard Penetration Test. 3. The error in the design method; this relates for example to using the blow count N for design purposes when N may not be entirely related to the ultimate capacity of a pile; this error could also be due to simplifying assumptions for a theoretical method. 4. The error in the load test due to the calibration of the jack or to the chosen failure criterion. 5. The error due to construction activities such as inadvertant batter, order of driving. The coefficients of variation presented in this article, and summarized in Table 8, correspond to the cummulation of errors 1 and 2.

Another part of the study dealt with the development of a design method for driven piles in sands which would include residual stresses (1). In the proposed method the ultimate capacity of the pile Q_u is calculated using the pile load test data base and correlations with the SPT blow count N:

$$Q_U = \left[A_p \times 19.75 \ (N)^{0.36}\right] + \left[A_f \times 0.224 \ (N)^{0.29}\right] \ \ . \ . \ . \ . \ (5)$$

TABLE 8.- Summary of Coefficients of Variation

Test	Coefficient of Variation (Horizontal)		Coefficient of Variation (Vertical)	
	Range	Average	Range	Average
SPT	0.144-0.770	0.421	0.164-1.148	0.707
PMT	0.282-0.682	0.416 (E) 0.399 (p_L)	0.516-0.783 0.261-0.575	0.619 (E) 0.503 (p_L)
CPT		Same order of magnitude as SPT and PMT		
SWVT		0.259		0.327
Density		0.057		

where A_p is the area of the pile point
         A_f is the area of the pile shaft

By using the same data base, the standard deviation of the ratio Q_U predicted over Q_U measured was calculated as 0.364 (1). The five errors mentioned earlier exist in the calculation of Q_U while errors 1 and 2 are involved in the value of N. It is of interest to find what portion of the error on Q_U is due to errors 1 and 2. Using the second order approximation of the Taylor series expansion for expected values, it comes:

$$\text{Var }(Q_U(N)) = \left[Q_U'(N) - \frac{1}{4}\left[(Q_U''(N)\right]^2 \text{var}(N)\right] \text{Var}(N) \ldots (6)$$

This leads to a coefficient of variation for Q_U equal to 0.13 for a 1 ft square, 50 ft long pile. These calculations show that errors 1 and 2 account for 36% of the total error on Q_U.

Conclusion

The statistical analysis of the results of 92 borings showed that at a given site the precision on the soil parameters measured with the SPT, PMT and CPT is approximately the same and that only the cross-hole shear wave velocity shear modulus shows an increased precision. However, the repeatability of the tests from one site to another and from one operator to another is not included in the above analysis and it is argued that the rating of repeatability of these tests would be; 1. Cross-hole shear wave velocity and cone penetrometer, 2. Pressuremeter, 3. Standard Penetration Test. Other factors not included in the above analysis and important to consider before choosing one test over another are whether the soil parameter measured is representative of the phenomenon to be predicted, whether the test is cost effective and whether the test can be performed in all soil conditions.

The coefficient of variation of the soil parameter was shown to increase with the size of the area tested and with the depth of testing. Also the coefficient of variation of the soil parameter in the vertical direction was equal to 1.5 times that in the horizontal direction on the average. It was shown in one specific example that there is little advantage to carrying out more than 6 SPT borings at one site.

Five errors involved with the prediction of ultimate pile capacity were identified. The errors due to natural soil heterogeneity and testing procedures accounted for 36% of the error in the prediction of pile capacity for the chosen method.

Acknowledgements

The results presented in this article are part of a study performed for the Federal Highway Administration and the United States Geological Survey under Contract No. DTFH 61-82-C-0038. The contact persons were Carl Ealy and Charles Smith. The team of researchers included H.M. Coyle, R.A. Hawkins, L.L. Lowery, R.L. Lytton, M.W. O'Neill.

REFERENCES

1. Briaud, J.-L., Tucker, L.M., Lytton, R.L., Coyle, H.M., "The Behavior of Piles and Pile Groups in Cohesionless Soils," Federal Highway Administration Report No. RD-82-38, October 1983.

2. Coyle, H.M., Bartoskewitz, R.E., and Berger, W.J., "Bearing Capacity Prediction by Wave Equation Analysis - State of the Art," Research Report No. 125-8, Texas Transportation Institute, Texas A&M University, August, 1973.

3. Fruco and Associates, "Pile Driving and Loading Tests," Report for Corps of Engineers, Little Rock, Arkansas, September, 1964.

4. Fruco and Associates, "Overwater Steel H-pile Driving and Testing Program," Report for Corps of Engineers, St. Louis, Missouri, September, 1973.

5. Gregersen, O.S., Aas, G., and DiBiaggio, E., "Load Tests on Friction Piles in Loose Sand," Proceedings of the VII International Conference on Soil Mechanics and Foundation Engineering, Moscow, Vol. 2.1, 1973, pp. 19-27.

6. Mansur, C.I., and Hunter, A.H., "Pile Tests - Arkansas River Project," Journal of the Soil Mechanics and Foundation Division, ASCE, Vol. 96, No. SM5, September, 1970, pp. 1545-1582.

7. Mansur, C.E., and Kaufman, R.I., "Pile Tests, Low-Sill Structure, Old River, Louisiana," Transactions of ASCE, Vol. 123, 1958, pp. 715-748.

8. Sellgren, E., "Friction Piles in Non-Cohesive Soils, Evluation from Pressuremeter Tests," Thesis, Chalmers University of Technology, Goteborg, Sweden, 1982.

9. Shannon & Wilson, Inc., "Geotechnical Engineering Studies: West Seattle Freeway Bridge Replacement," Report for Anderson-Bjornstad-Kane-Jacobs, Inc., Vol. 2, August, 1980.

10. Shannon & Wilson, Inc., "Instrumentation Installation and Initial Monitoring Pier EA-31," Report for City of Seattle, FHWA (Progress Report 1), November, 1982.

11. Tavenas, F.A., "Load Tests on Friction Piles in Sand," Canadian Geotechnical Journal, Vol. 8, No. 7, 1971, pp. 7-22.

12. Tucker, L.M., "The Behavior of Piles in Cohesionless Soils," Master of Science Thesis, Civil Engineering Department, Texas A&M University, December 1983.

13. Vesic, A.S., "A Study of Bearing Capacity of Deep Foundations," Project B-189, (Final Report), Georgia Institute of Technology, August, 1966.

14. Vesic, A.S., "Tests on Instrumented Piles, Ogeechee River Site," Journal of the Soil Mechanics and Foundation Divisions, ASCE, Vol. 96, No. SM2, March, 1970, pp. 561-583.

15. Woodward-Clyde Consultants, "Results and Interpretation of Pile Driving Effects Test Program," Phase IV Report for Corps of Engineers, Vol. III, St. Louis, Missouri, July, 1979.

16. Woodward-Clyde Consultants, "Axial Load Tests Monoliths M5 and M6," Supplemental Report to Corps of Engineers, St. Louis, Missouri, February, 1980.

PROBABILISTIC CHARACTERIZATION OF
NIGERIAN SOILS

Samuel Uche Ejezie,[1] A. M. ASCE
Kingsley Harrop-Williams,[2] A. M. ASCE

ABSTRACT

A probabilistic method of subsurface characterization is developed for sites in Southern Nigeria. This method is based on the use of statistics to analyze real field data and determine models for predicting data trends in similar environments. The method is used to confirm the validity of an existing classification scheme for the soils in the area. This scheme recognizes four major soil groups in addition to some specific or local soil types found in different locations.

Through the application of the probabilistic method of analysis these groups and subgroups of soils in Southern Nigeria are shown to be characterized by peculiar trends in properties defined by specific probability distribution models. In general, the variations of all the soil properties can be modelled by the common probability density functions. Apparently, all the available data show some measure of skewness. In addition, most properties display such regular patterns that models predicted from quantitative analysis of the data agree with the shapes of the corresponding histograms.

The models developed incoporate all factors contributing to soil property variations and can thus be used with confidence in all engineering designs and analyses.

INTRODUCTION

This paper focuses on Southern Nigeria, a typical area of the Humid Tropical West African Region, as shown in the insert in figure 1. The soils here, like soils found in other tropical areas, are characterized by complex physical, chemical and engineering properties. These have appreciable adverse effects on the reliability of geotechnical design decisions in this area. The soil properties vary erratically. The engineering behavior of the soils is remarkably inconsistent and generally difficult to predict using conventional soil mechanics approaches. These problems are a reflection of the great influence of climate on the soils. Tropical climate subjects the soils to intense post-formation alterations such as those resulting from the

---

[1]Doctoral Candidate, Department of Civil Engineering, Carnegie–Mellon University, Pittsburgh, Pennsylvania 15213

[2]Assistant Professor, Department of Civil Engineering, Carnegie–Mellon University, Pittsburgh, Pennsylvania 15213

high temperatures and heavy rainfall typical of this climate.

In view of the apparent uncertainties surrounding the behavior of the soils, there is need for the development of a probabilistic method of subsurface characterization for sites in the study area. This objective is achieved in this paper by analyzing real field data on the soil properties and determining the appropriate probabilistic models for predicting data trends in similar environments. Furthermore, the probabilistic method will confirm the validity of the existing classification scheme for soils in the area.

Previous Work

The volume of published work on the soils of Southern Nigeria is relatively small. However, some of the available information relevant in this study is contained in the works of Ackroyd [1], Madu [10] [11] [12], Jackson [8], Ejezie [3], and Ejezie et. al. [4]. In addition, some useful information is available in the form of unpublished reports of engineering projects carried out in different parts of the area. Notable among these are those by Nigerian Foundation Servises and Soils Research Company Limited [13] [14].

The majority of these previous works dealt with soils in selected parts of Southern Nigeria. Nevertheless, Ejezie [3] and Ejezie et. al. [4] present a broad picture for the soils in the entire area. This paper follows the same format, utilizing data from different parts of the area to formulate a probabilistic framework for predicting soil properties and subsurface characteristics. The soil classification scheme developed for this area by Ejezie [3] is shown to be valid and representative of actual diversifications in the soil types.

CLASSIFICATION AND PROPERTIES OF SOUTHERN NIGERIAN SOILS

The geological setting of Southern Nigeria has been well-described and documented by the Nigerian Geological Survey, and also by Reyment [15]. The bedrock comprises two main lithologic groups namely the Basement Complex and the Sedimentary Formations. The associated rock types have been subjected to the influence of tropical weathering. The resulting soils are varied and depend on the nature of the underlying parent rocks. The Basement Complex yields soils that contain weatherable minerals and are susceptible to deep leaching, particularly in areas with sufficient rainfall and adequate residual soil permeability. The Sedimentary Formations yield soils generally consisting of relatively stable secondary minerals and resistant primary minerals which weather very slowly, resulting in mineral leaching not extending to great depths [4].

Soil Classification

A comprehensive classification scheme has been developed by Ejezie [3] for these soils. This scheme distinguishes four major soil groups on the basis of general areal distribution pattern and similarity or correlation of properties. Within each group some local soil types or sub-groups are also identified by this scheme. The major soil groups include: Recent Deposits, Non-concretionary Acid Sands and Clays, Soils derived from Early- to Mid-Cretaceous Sandstones and Shales, and Ferruginous Tropical Soils. Figure 1 shows a map of Southern Nigeria and the approximate extents of these soil groups. This figure generally delimits boundaries within which

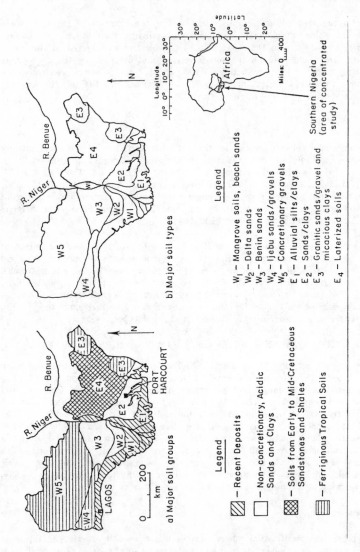

Figure 1: Soil Groups of Southern Nigeria (After Ejezie,[3])

particular soil groups are predominant; hence, it is common for a specific soil type to span across a group boundary.

Soil Properties

The soils of Southern Nigeria exhibit property trends typical of a humid tropical environment. The tropical climate is the most important factor which influences the processes of soil formation. In addition, this climate controls the post-formation alterations to which the soils are subjected, and hence, the chemical, physicochemical, textural and engineering properties exhibited by the soils. The climate in this area is marked by two well-defined yearly seasons on the basis of rainfall distribution, namely, the wet and the dry seasons. The duration of the seasons, the intensity of the rains and the temperature ranges vary widely from one area to the other. Correspondingly, the soils in these areas display highly variable and complex properties.

The influence of climate on the soil properties is explained in terms of tropical weathering and the associated processes of leaching and changes in chemical composition and mineralogy. Weatherable minerals disintegrate fast under this climate and are easily flushed out by infiltrating rainwater, resulting in the development of well-defined soil profiles common in this area. This process culminates in the removal of silica in colloidal form, the disintegration of aluminosilicate clay minerals and the accumulation of sesquioxides and hydroxides of iron and aluminum. This is the well-known phenomenon of laterization. It gives rise to several trends in property which are of significance in geotechnical engineering, such as increase (or sometimes decrease) in porosity and void ratio; changes in density, permeability, and compressibility; and vertical variations of strength characteristics of soils in various horizons.

Table 1 gives a general summary of the properties of soils in Southern Nigeria according to the major soil groups. Microvariations within groups are generally not considered in this table except where they are pronounced and account for major deviations in property trends.

VARIABILITY OF SOIL PROPERTIES

In order to adequately illustrate the variability of the properties of soils in Southern Nigeria, this paper focusses on the plasticity characteristics, strength and consolidation characteristics, and unit weight (or in-situ density) of these soils.

The plasticity characteristics vary erratically both in space and time, and from one soil type to the other. Since they reflect the behavior of the soils in relation to the amount of water present in the system, they generally are affected by clay content, organic matter content, the soil fabric, and the nature of the exchangeable cations. The degree of influence of these factors on tropical soils has been investigated by Terzaghi [16], Gidigasu [5], and other researchers. In addition, plasticity values for tropical soils have been shown to be appreciably affected by methods of pre-test sample preparations and testing procedures, such as air-drying and remolding, which decrease and increase plasticity respectively [16].

The strength and consolidation characteristics of the soils are substantially variable. They are controlled by the amount of sesquioxide and hydroxide cements

Table 1: Major Soil Groups of Southern Nigeria: Summary of Properties
(After Ejezie, et. al.[4])

Soil Group	Chemical Composition	Physicochemical Properties	Textural Properties	Engineering Properties
Recent Deposits	Minerals from primary weathering and resistant mineral fragments; oxides of parent materials.	Neutral pH(about 7.0)*; low to high organic matter content and cation exchange capacity; variable hygroscopic moisture content.	Fine-grained, with occasional sand and gravel; fabric varies from single-grained to deflocculated clay aggregates; general lack of cement except for clay and organic matter binders.	Low to medium plasticity(PI values range from 9% to 51%)*; variable in-situ density(10.6 - 19.6kN/m^3)*, with sandy deposits giving higher values; widely varying permeability; low strength for clay deposits and relatively higher for granular deposits(unconfined compressive strength range for clays in the Calabar River Swamp: 4.0 - 34.0 kN/m^2)*; Some highly compressible clay deposits, with compression index ranges from 0.18 to 0.50*.
Non-concretionary Acid Sands and Clays	Minerals: kaolinite, illite, quartz, feldspars, traces of vermiculite, and montmorillonite; Oxides: hematite, goethite, and gibbsite.	Low pH(4.3)**; low organic matter content (below 2.0%)**;very low cation exchange capacity, and hygroscopic moisture content(0.15 - 0.7%)**.	Poorly-graded fine to medium sand; single-grained fabric; little hydrated ferric oxide cement.	Very low to non-plastic; variable in-situ density; high permeability; frequently low strength; low compressibility; occasional instability of exposed hillsides; extensive gullying.
Soils Derived from Early to Mid-Cretaceous Sandstones and Shales.	Minerals: montmorillonite, illite, vermiculite, quartz, traces of feldspar, and micas; Oxides: silica, alumina, iron oxides; also minor amounts of potassium, sodium, magnesium, calcium and titanium oxides.	Low pH(4.3 - 5.7)**; moderate organic matter content(3 - 8%)**; low cation exchange capacity(21 - 45)**; and moderately low and variable hygroscopic moisture content(0.6 - 9.8%)**.	Well-graded; single-grained structure; concretionary due to laterization; hydrated ferric oxide cement; relict bedding and grain orientations.	Plasticity ranges from medium to low to non-plastic(PI range: /-42%)*; medium to high density; variable permeability; field strength performance much better than predictions based on laboratory tests(typical range of field vane strength: 22 - 109 kN/m^2)*; very low compressibility.

Table 1 (contonued)

Soil Group	Chemical Composition	Physicochemical Properties	Textural Properties	Engineering Properties
Ferruginous Tropical Soils	Minerals: kaolinite, quartz, feldspar, some ferromagnessian minerals; Oxides: large quantities of free sesquioxides, hematite, goethite.	High pH, low organic matter content, moderately low to very low cation exchange capacity, and moderately low hygroscopic moisture content.	Well-graded; single-grained fabric, aggregated grains of clay platelets, sand particles with surface coatings of clay; sesquioxide and hydroxide cements; relict mineral cleavage and form preserved by finely crystallized sesquioxide skeletons.	Non-plastic to moderately plastic(typical PI range: 9-28%)*; variable in-situ density(typical range: 10.2-18.0 kN/m^2)* and permeability controlled by cementation; high strength with low strain at failure(unconfined compressive strength range: 47-190 kN/m^2)*; very low compressibility which depends on moisture content.

*From reports prepared by Nigerian Foundation Services & Soils Research Company limited, for Louis Berger International Inc. (13, 14)

**From Madu, (10, 11, 12)

present in the soil structure. The higher the amount of cement, the higher the strength and lower the compressibility. However, when the soil is water-saturated or remolded, the cement bond is weakened, the particles disaggregate, thus increasing the clay fraction, decreasing the strength, and increasing the compressibility.

The unit weight or in-situ density is controlled by the extent of weathering or decomposition of the soil parent materials as well as the degree of laterization of the residual soils. The increase in void ratio and porosity which accompanies leaching, causes a decrease in density. The subsequent laterization, however, increases the density. In a given soil type, the density varies both vertically down the profile and laterally throughout the area of occurrence.

The foregoing discussion shows that the properties of soils in Southern Nigeria are randomly variable and therefore constitute a problem amenable to statistical and probabilistic solutions.

Statistical Analyses of Data

The parameters considered in these analyses include: the natural moisture content, liquid limit, plasticity index, undrained shear strength (Unconfined Compression, Pocket Penetrometer, Torvane, Field Vane), compression ratio, and in-situ density. The available data are separated into populations corresponding to specific subdivisions or units of the major soil groups in the area. The sample statistics, namely, the mean, standard deviation, and coefficient of variation are determined for each data set. These are summarized in Table 2.

The coefficient of variation, defined as the ratio of the standard deviation to the mean value, is a non-dimentional measure of variance. As a result, it can be used to compare the relative variation of soil parameters with different dimensional measures. It has also been observed to remain fairly fixed for specific soil properties, such that several authors [7] [9] have recommended specific coefficients of variation for various soil properties. Based on this, it can be concluded that the coefficients of variation listed in Table 2 give a basic idea of values to expect for soils in different parts of Southern Nigeria.

The table also reveals important trends in properties of the specific soil units or subgroups in the area. For example, the plasticity characteristics of Estuarine Deposits and Tidal Swamp Soils appear to be no more random than those of soils derived from Early- to Mid-Cretaceous rocks. However, they are comparatively more random than the characteristics of Soft Clays and Ferruginous Tropical Soils. The strength of the Ferruginous Tropical Soils is also seen to be less random than that of Soils from Early- to Mid-Cretaceous rocks and the Recent Deposits. Lee et. al. [9] have summarized the recommended coefficients of variation of these properties for conventional soils. Typical values are: 0.15 for moisture content, 0.10 for liquid limit and plastic limit, 0.40 for unconfined compressive strength, 0.03 for unit weight, and 0.30 for compressibility. Hence, it is seen that except for the Soft Clays, these properties are more varied for Nigerian Soils. The apparent conformity of the Soft Clays to conventional behavior can be explained by the fact that these soils are relatively non-laterized, hence, they are not significantly different than clays found in the Temperate region.

Table 2: Variability of Soil Parameters

Major Soil Group		Recent Deposits			Soils Derived from Early-to Mid-Cretaceous Rocks				Ferruginous Tropical Soils
Soil Unit or Sub-group		Soft Clays	Estuarine Deposits	Tidal Swamp Soils	Soils over Early-Cretaceous Rocks	Soils over Early-Mid-Cret. Rocks	Soils over Basement/Sed. boundary	Mixture of all 3 Units	
Natural moisture content (%)	# of samples	29	32	36				29	17
	Range	49-195	3-101	13-210				5-92	7-29
	Mean	105.1	38.0	71.1	-			24.2	18.5
	Std. Dev.	30.8	33.1	57.7				20.5	5.6
	Coeff.Var.	0.29	0.87	0.81				0.85	0.30
Liquid limit (%)	# of samples	38	11	31	21	20	10	51	15
	Range	70-103	15-66	23-89	23-84	21-75	21-56	21-84	22-57
	Mean	89.4	38.5	50.2	55.5	41.3	33.0	45.5	42.1
	Std. Dev.	6.7	21.0	20.0	21.4	15.3	11.3	19.4	9.8
	Coeff.Var.	0.08	0.55	0.40	0.39	0.37	0.34	0.43	0.23
Plasticity index (%)	# of samples	38	7	31	21	20	10	51	15
	Range	35-51	10-37	9-44	9-42	7-35	9-27	7-42	9-28
	Mean	43.8	19.9	22.7	25.6	18.6	15.2	20.8	15.7
	Std. dev.	3.8	9.0	9.6	11.2	7.9	6.1	9.9	5.1
	Coeff.Var.	0.09	0.45	0.42	0.44	0.43	0.40	0.48	0.33
** UC/PP/FV Strength property (kN/m²)	# of samples	38 (UC)	-	16 (dd)	-	-	-	20 (FV)	53 (UC)
	Range	3-33		13-241				22-109	47-190
	Mean	12.1		79.4				68.9	135.9
	Std. Dev.	6.7		76.4				31.5	37.4
	Coeff.Var.	0.56		0.96				0.45	0.28
Torvane Strength property (kN/m²)	# of samples	35	-	15	-	-	-	-	-
	Range	7-24		7-64					
	Mean	13.0		31.5					
	Std. Dev.	4.4		17.0					
	Coeff.Var.	0.34		0.54					

SOIL PARAMETERS

** UC = Unconfined Compressive Strength, PP = Pocket Penetrometer, FV = Field Vane.

Table 2 (continued)

Major Soil Group		Recent Deposits			Soils Derived From Early- to Mid-Cretaceous Rocks				Ferruginous Tropical Soils
Soil Unit or Sub-group		Soft Clays	Estuarine Deposits	Tidal Swamp Soils	Soils over Early-Creta-ceous Rocks	Soils over Mid-Cret. Rocks	Soils over Basement/Sed. boundary	Mixture of all 3 Units	
Unit Weight (kN/m³)	# of sampls	31		17					5
	Range	12-15		11-20					10-18
	Mean	13.9	–	16.7	–	–	–	–	15.3
	Std. Dev.	0.66		3.27					3.13
	Coeff.Var	0.05		0.20					0.20
Compress-ion Ratio	# of sampls	18							
	Range	0.2-0.5		–					–
	Mean	0.33	–						
	Std. Dev.	0.08							
	Coeff.Var	0.24							

SOIL PARAMETERS

PROBABILISTIC ANALYSIS OF SOIL PROPERTIES

The results in Table 2 illustrate the behavior of the first and second moment characteristics of the properties of these tropical soils of Southern Nigeria. These moments represent the central value and the variation about the central value of these properties. However, in order to model the true behavior of these properties the probability distributions governing each property must be developed. The information available generally cannot allow the theoretical development of the probability distribution and it must in some way be approximated. This is usually done by fitting one of the conventional probability distributions (e.g., normal, lognormal, gamma, or beta) to the data. Although these are two parameter distributions that can be formulated based on the first two moments of the variable, the shape of the chosen distribution should reflect the skewness (3rd moment) and kurtosis (4th moment) of the property. Figure 2 illustrates the shapes of the histograms produced by the samples of selected properties. These portray the remarkable manner in which the observed occurrences of the values of the properties vary.

Model Predictions

In this section an attempt is made to determine which of the four conventional distributions best represents the specific properties subject to the information available in the sample. Two different approaches are adopted. The first is the Pearson's method of selecting appropriate distributions [7], [6], and the second is the Kolmogorov-Smirnov Test for comparing selected distributions [2].

The Pearson's method involves the determination of the coefficients of skewness (β_1) and kurtosis (β_2). The skewness coefficient is defined as the ratio of the square of the third central moment to the cube of the variance, while the coefficient of kurtosis is defined as the ratio of the fourth central moment to the square of the variance. A parameter, K, is next introduced as a function of β_1 and β_2 as follows:

$$K = \beta_1(\beta_2+3)^2/4(2\beta_2-3\beta_1-6)(4\beta_2-3\beta_1)$$

The K value is then used to select the specific distribution type that best represents the sampled data. The distinction of the specific types is as follows:

Symmetrical

K = −∞	K < 0	K = 0	0 < K < 1	K = 1		K = +∞
Type III	Type I	Normal (β_2=3) Type II, β_2<3 Type VII, β_2>3	Type IV	Type V	Type VI	Type III

The Pearson's system predicts the Beta distribution if K < 0 (Type 1), Gamma if K = ±∞ (Type III), Lognormal if K = 1 (Type V), and Normal if K = 0 and β_2 = 3 (transition between Types II and VII).

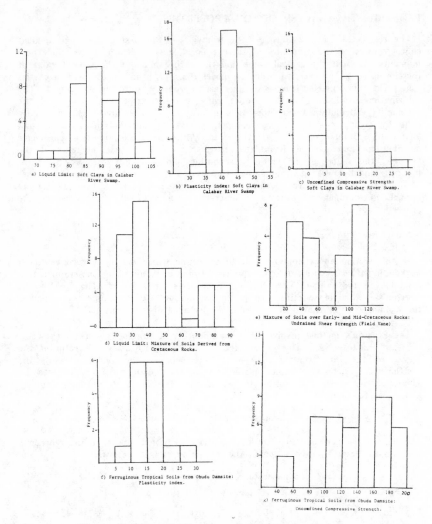

Figure 2: Typical Histograms of Soil Properties
in Southern Nigeria

The skewness, kurtosis and K coefficients of the soil properties under investigation are shown in Table 3. The values indicate that most of the properties of the Nigerian soils can be modelled by the Beta distribution based on the Pearson's system. This may be due particularly to the relatively small size of the statistical samples as well as the versatility of the Beta distribution in changing its shape while constrained within the observed extremes of the sample. However, this is not a feature unique to the soils in this area. The same properties for temperate soils have also been classified as Beta distributed by the Pearson's system [7].

Although the Pearson's system predicts the Beta distribution for most of the soil properties it is also observed that some appear close to normal ($\beta_1=0$, $\beta_2=3$). This prompted further analysis in this work to show how the goodness of fit of the Beta distribution compared with the others using the Kolmogorov-Smirnov statistic. This statistic is defined as:

$$D_2 = \underset{x}{\mathrm{Max}} \left| F(x) - S_n(x) \right| \quad ,$$

where $F(x)$ is the cummulative distribution of the tested probability model and $S_n(x)$ is the experimental cummulative frequency function. Thus D_2 is the maximum of the absolute values of this difference over the entire range of x. If two distributions are evaluated by this test the one with the smaller D_2 is selected. Table 4 lists the D_2 values as they correspond to the Beta, Normal, Gamma and Lognormal distributions when fitted to the properties of the soils of Southern Nigeria. The asterisks indicate the recommended model as predicted by this test. These results are different than those predicted by Pearson's system, with the majority of the properties conforming to the Beta and Lognormal distributions. This difference is due probably to the method of testing. Whereas the Pearson's system compares the skewness and kurtosis of the proposed distributions with those of the sample, the Kolmogorov-Smirnov Test compares the difference in probability predictions of the proposed and experimental distributions.

The statistic, D_2, is a random variable dependent on the size of the sample. Tabulated critical values of D_2 for specific significance levels are available [2]. This proves very useful in the determination of the suitability of a chosen distribution for modelling a specific property. The values recorded in Table 4 indicate that all the soil properties can be modelled by the Beta distribution at the 5% significant level.

DISCUSSION OF ENGINEERING APPLICATIONS

The variability of soil parameters in the study area complicates the conventional geotechnical engineering design process. The standard practice of choosing design values of soil properties from a limited amount of data rarely yields representative values. This is especially true for tropical soils due to the larger variability experienced when compared with temperate soils. This variability is quantified in this paper and probability models are proposed for the random parameters of these humid tropical soils. These probability models, in turn, enhance the design process by allowing the determination of design values of the soil parameters at specific confidence levels.

The results shown in Table 2 reinforce the existing classification scheme of Southern Nigerian soils [3]. In general, the different subgroups can be

Table 3: Probability Models Determined by Pearson's System

Major Soil Group		Recent Deposits			Soils Derived from Early- to Mid-Cretaceous Rocks				Ferruginois Tropical Soils
Soil Unit or Sub-group		Soft Clays	Estuarine Deposits	Tidal Swamp Soils	Soils over Early Cret. Rocks	Soils over Mid-Cret. Rocks	Soils over Basement/Sed. boundary	Mixture of all 3 Cret.Units	
Natural moisture content (%)	B1	1.28	0.614	0.671	–		–	3.306	0.000
	B2	4.40	1.997	2.436				5.978	2.633
	K	-1.21	-0.162	-0.204				-1.201	0.000
	Model Type	I	I	I				I	II
Liquid limit (%)	B1	0.219	0.005	0.216	0.010	0.640	0.625	0.505	0.152
	B2	3.512	1.341	2.059	1.475	2.773	2.606	2.291	2.474
	K	0.470	-0.001	-0.072	-0.003	-0.245	-0.216	-0.158	-0.080
	Model Type	IV	I or II	I	I or II	I	I	I	I
Plasticity index (%)	B1	0.064	0.584	0.266	0.043	0.241	0.484	0.504	1.036
	B2	2.786	2.849	2.233	1.626	2.285	2.372	2.468	3.470
	K	-0.079	-0.252	-0.096	-0.013	-0.093	-0.160	-0.175	-0.464
	Model Type	I	I	I	I	I	I	I	I
** UC/PP/FV Strength property (kN/m²)	B1	1.453 ⎫UC	–	0.640 ⎫dd	–		–	0.018 ⎫FV	0.357 ⎫UC
	B2	4.230		2.320				1.520	2.669
	K	-0.796 ⎭		-0.188 ⎭				-0.005 ⎭	-0.172 ⎭
	Model Type	I		I				I	I
Torvane Strength property (kN/m²)	B1	0.265	–	0.008	–		–	–	–
	B2	2.710		2.312					
	K	-0.156		-0.004					
	Model Type	I		I or II					
Unit Weight (kN/m³)	B1	0.036	–	0.677	–	–	–	–	0.837
	B2	2.978		2.111					2.487
	K	-0.178		-0.181					-0.239
	Model Type	I		I					I
Compression Ratio	B1	1.462		–	–	–	–	–	–
	B2	2.383							
	K	-0.081							
	Model Type	I							

** UC = Unconfined Compressive Strength, PP = Pocket Penetrometer, FV = Field Vane.

Table 4: Kolmogorov-Smirnov Test Statistic

Soil Unit or Sub-group (Parameter)	Sub-group	Soft Clays	Estuarine Deposits	Tidal Swamp Soils	Soils over Early-Cretaceous Rocks	Soils over Mid-Cret. Rocks	Soils over Basement/Sed. boundary	Mixture of all 3 Cret.Units	Ferruginous Tropical Soils
Natural moisture content (%)	Beta	0.178	0.176	0.117*	–	–	–	0.186	0.131
	Normal	0.204	0.225*	0.243				0.228	0.092
	Gama	0.162*	0.147*	0.222				0.117	0.067*
	Lognormal	0.148*	0.212	0.287				0.097*	0.065*
Liquid limit (%)	Beta	0.100	0.130*	0.077*	0.140*	0.120	0.121*	0.101	0.107
	Normal	0.083	0.218	0.100	0.153	0.160	0.202	0.141	0.064*
	Gama	0.081*	0.247	0.087	0.165	0.112	0.174	0.098	0.073
	Lognormal	0.083	0.287	0.102	0.174	0.093*	0.169	0.085*	0.087
Plasticity index (%)	Beta	0.146	0.233	0.093*	0.090*	0.126	0.200	0.077*	0.141
	Normal	0.111	0.256	0.151	0.133	0.180	0.156*	0.141	0.154
	Gama	0.101	0.202*	0.097	0.119	0.129	0.138*	0.090	0.112*
	Lognormal	0.096*	0.177*	0.105	0.134	0.110	0.143	0.077*	0.094*
++ UC/PP/FV Strength property (kN/m²)	Beta	0.116	–	0.125*	–	–	–	0.106*	0.086*
	Normal	0.152		0.260				0.121	0.126
	Gama	0.075		0.220				0.143	0.163
	Lognormal	0.074*		0.312				0.162	0.180
Torvane Strength property (kN/m²)	Beta	0.104	–	0.158	–	–	–	–	–
	Normal	0.120		0.129*					
	Gama	0.082*		0.158					
	Lognormal	0.088		0.199					
Unit Weight (kN/m³)	Beta	0.136	–	0.201	–	–	–	–	0.230
	Normal	0.091		0.195*					0.201
	Gama	0.131		0.214					0.197
	Lognormal	0.084*		0.226					0.189*
Compression Ratio	Beta	0.147	–	–	–	–	–	–	–
	Normal	0.157							
	Gama	0.125							
	Lognormal	0.109*							

++ UC = Unconfined Compressive Strength, PP = Pocket Penetrometer, FV = Field Vane.

* Predicted probability model

distinguished by their coefficients of variation. The Soft Clays of the Recent Deposits, being relatively non-laterized, behave similar to clays of temperate regions. Also the properties of the Ferruginous Tropical Soils are considerably less random than those of soils derived from Early- to Mid-Cretaceous rocks, which in turn are less random than those of Recent Estuarine and Tidal Swamp soils. This trend corresponds to the degree of laterization in these soil groups, hence it can be concluded that the more advanced the stage of laterization a soil has experienced, the less the variability of the properties. This conclusion agrees with field observations which show that highly laterized soil profiles are remarkably more stable than profiles of soils under intermediate stages of laterization.

Tables 3 and 4 suggest that most of the properties of these tropical soils can be modelled by the beta distribution. This is in conformity with studies performed on corresponding properties of temperate soils.

CONCLUSION

The soils of Southern Nigeria in particular and the Humid tropical region in general show a high degree of variability in their properties which has been attributed to the influence of the Tropical climate. The soils are altered by the processes of weathering and leaching which are preludes to the laterization process. Correspondingly, the properties are affected and show remarkable deviations from expected conventional trends.

A probabilistic analysis of data on the properties of these soils has revealed that most of the properties can be modelled by the beta distribution. In addition, it quantified the variation of specific properties. It is particularly noteworthy that Tables 2, 3 and 4 provide information that can be used to determine confidence levels for selected design values of these properties.

Furthermore, the probabilistic analysis has reinforced the validity of the proposed soil classification scheme for Southern Nigeria. Most of the soil groups and units distinguished in the area represent distinct trends in statistical properties.

APPENDIX-1: REFERENCES

[1]   Ackroyd, L. W.
      Formation and Properties of Concretionary and Non-concretionary Soils in
          Western Nigeria.
      In A. Burgers, J. S. Greg, S. M. Lloyd and A. D. W. Sparks (editors),
      *Proceedings of the 4th Regional Conference for Africa on Soil
      Mechanics and Foundation Engineering, Vol.1*, pages 47-52. 1967.

[2]   Ang, Alfredo H-S. and Tang, Wilson H.
      Probability Concepts in Engineering Planning and Design.
      John Wiley and Sons, Inc., 1975.

[3]   Ejezie, S. U.
      Engineering Characterization of Soils of Southern Nigeria.
      Master's thesis, School of Civil and Environmental Engineering, Cornell
      University, January, 1982.

[4]   Ejezie, S. U., O'Rourke, T. D. and Harrop-Williams, K.
       Remote Sensing Characterization of Nigerian Soils.
       In *ASCE Geotechnical Symposium, Technical Session on Geologic
       Environment and Soil Properties.* American Society of Civil Engineers,
       Geotechnical Engineering Division, October, 1983.

[5]   Gidigasu, M. D.
       9: Laterite Soil Engineering, Developments in Geotechnical Engineering.
       Elsevier Publishing Company, 1976.

[6]   Hahn, G. J. and Shapiro, S. S.
       Statistical Models in Engineering.
       John Wiley and Sons, Inc., 1967.

[7]   Harr, M. E.
       Mechanics of Particulate Media - A Probabilistic Approach.
       McGraw-Hill, Inc., 1977.

[8]   Jackson, J. O.
       The Failure of Foundations in Coastal Plains Sands.
       In *Proceedings of the 7th Regional Conference for Africa on Soil
       Mechanics and Foundation Engineering, Vol.1*, pages 261-268. June,
       1980.

[9]   Lee, I. K., White, W. and Ingles, O. C.
       Geotechnical Engineering.
       Pitman Publishing Inc., 1983.

[10]   Madu, R. M.
       Some Nigerian Residual Soils - Their Characteristics and Relative Road
       Building Properties on a Group Basis.
       In P. J. N. Pells and A. M. G. Robertson (editors), *Proceedings of the 6th
       Regional Conference for Africa on Soil Mechanics and Foundation
       Engineering, Vol.1*, pages 121-129. 1975.

[11]   Madu, R. M.
       An Investigation into the Geotechnical and Engineering Properties of some
       Laterites of Eastern Nigeria.
       Engineering Geology 11(2):101-125, 1976.

[12]   Madu, R. M.
       The Use of The Chemical and Physicochemical Properties of Laterites in
       their Identification.
       In *Proceedings of the 7th Regional Conference for Africa on Soil
       Mechanics and Foundation Engineering, Vol. 1*, pages 105-116. 1980.

[13]   NFSSRC (Nigerian Foundation Services and Soils Research Company
       Limited).
       Calabar-Cross Highway: Final Report on the Soils Investigations and the
       Design and Construction of Embankment through the Calabar River
       Swamp.
       1975.

[14] NFSSRC (Nigerian Foundation Services and Soils Research Company
      Limited).
      Report on Subsurface Investigations at the Ikom Dam Site.
      1978.

[15] Reyment, R. A.
      Aspects of the Geology of Nigeria.
      Ibadan University Press, University of Ibadan, Ibadan, Nigeria, 1965.

[16] Terzaghi, K.
      Design and Performance of Sasumua Dam.
      In *Proceedings if the Institution of Civil Engineers, Vol. 9*, pages 369-394.
          Institution of Civil Engineers, April, 1958.

An Extreme-Value Model for
Strength of Stiff Clays

Kalankamary P. George*, and Adnan A. Basma**

Abstract: This study highlights a statistical theory of failure for
stiff fissured clays. The failure in these clays is a process characteristic of the "defect" structure; accordingly, it is shown that their
strength or bearing capacity is determined by the smallest value of the
failure strength. A minimum extremal type distribution (Weibull distribution) is found to represent statistically the strength of such
deposits. Weibull distribution not only fits the published data on
London clay (11) but also portrays the characteristic "size effect"
of fissured clays. The authors contend this result to be step for-
ward in the direction of replacing the empirical factors, as recommended by previous researchers, in estimating field strength from
laboratory results.

The role of the distribution function in the safety analysis of
soil structures is briefly discussed. Comparison of the two statistical distributions - normal and Weibull - reveals that Weibull distribution, because of its emphasis on defect structure gives rise to
relatively conservative designs in fissured clays.

Introduction

Reliability of soil structures depends on the strength of the soil
and the loading imposed as well as their variability. This latter
aspect, however, is largely overlooked in conventional design practice.
Basically, the conventional approach seeks to minimize the maximum
tolerable risk. Estimated lower limits of strength and upper limits
of loading are often considered to occur simultaneously and at critical
locations.

There are two main and, in general, complementary approaches to a
complete understanding of the strength properties of soils. The first
of these, and the one to which the major effort has been devoted, is
the examination of shearing strength in a macroscopic strength test.
The second approach concentrates on the study of the fundamental aspects
of interparticle behavior. Only in relatively few investigations has
this latter approach been employed.

---

*Prof., Dept. of Civ. Engrg., The Univ. of Mississippi, University,
MS, 38677.

**Graduate Research Assistant, The Univ. of Mississippi, University,
MS, 38677.

A large number of parameters affect the strength of cohesive soil. Thus, the most important tests from which the macroscopic soil behavior can be deduced are those performed on one soil prepared in a consistent fashion from test to test. However, because natural soils, even those of the same type taken from the same deposit, vary, large differences can occur in tests performed on different batches of apparently similar soils. Such variation is even more prevalent in overconsolidated, stiff fissured clays which are very complex materials and are often difficult to sample and test.

In his pioneering work, Lumb (10) showed that strength parameters of clays appear to follow a normal distribution. Schultz (16) corroborated Lumb's assertion that some soil parameters are normal-like variates. He observed, however, very high coefficient of variation for the unconfined compressive strength. Marsland (11), in his studies of stiff fissured clay stated: "In spite of the most careful sampling and specimen preparation the scatter of test results on 1.5 in. (38 mm) diameter specimens at each test level was very large and it was considered that an explanation of this variation was required before the use of average values could be justified." Because the minimum strength rather than the average strength is significant in the safety analysis, a distribution theory for minima has been employed in such materials as mild steel (14) and concrete (21). Asymtotic distribution of the smallest values, otherwise known as "weakest-link" yielding the Weibull distribution, is the key concept employed in those analyses. Whether the Weibull theory gives a better representation of the strength of stiff fissured clays than the normal distribution is the primary objective of this paper.

With stiff fissured clays, yet another problem is how to relate the strength measured in the laboratory to the full-scale strength applicable to engineering problems. The influence of sample size on measured strength, otherwise known as "size effect" on material strength, has been known for more than a centruy (8). By size effect, we mean that the strength of a piece of material decreases with an increase in dimensions in a way which is typical for the type and homogeneity of material. Scale effect, in general, tends to be significant as material variability increases. Scale effect is more pronounced in brittle materials than in ductile materials.

Recent studies have emphasized the importance of scale effect in fissured clays (2, 11, 13). In order for the results of standard laboratory tests to be used in design, Whitaker and Cooke (20), and Rowe (15) introduced a factor to reduce average values obtained from these tests to give the equivalent "fissured" or large-scale strengths. Skempton (17) pointed out that this empirical factor would vary with the type of test, the size of specimen, and the technique used to obtain the samples. In estimating ultimate pile capacity in stiff fissured clays, Meyerhof (13) recognized scale effect and established an empirical reduction factor to be applied to the undrained shear strength determined from triaxial compression tests. This review highlights the fact that size effect is pronounced in stiff fissured (overconsolidated) clays and is largely influenced by the degree of heterogeneity resulting from the inherent variability of constituent particles

and/or flaws (cracks) in the material. This study has as its objectives
the development of an adequate theoretical basis for such a size effect
and the testing of its validity by comparing it with experimental results ascertained from the literature. Lastly, how structural reliability predictions are affected by the Weibull theory is illustrated
with an example.

Weibull Theory and Breaking Strength

    Because of variations in natural soils, even those of the same type
taken from the same deposit, large differences can occur in tests performed on different batches of apparently similar soils. Such scatter
is prevalent in overconsolidated, stiff fissured clays and is generally
incorporated in design by treating it as a random variable and statistical representation by an appropriate distribution function (d.f.).
Normal and lognormal distribution functions have been proposed in
earlier research studies (10). Unfortunately, these two d.f.s emphasize
strength values in the central region of the distribution; consequently,
the tail probabilities are not adequately described. For example, in
the lognormal probability function, the probability of survival as a
function of the logarithm of the stress approaches unity in the same
way as it approaches zero, a situation which is contradicted by the
experimental fact.

    Instead of normal and lognormal theories, we use the theory of
extreme values, the application of which may be justified as follows:
the difference between the calculated (determined from strength theory)
and the observed strength resides in the existence of weakening flaws.
Therefore, a different amount of force will be needed to fail the material at one point or another. In materials such as stiff fissured
clays characterized by weakening fissures, failure at one point means
failure of the entire specimen. This fact simply means statistically
that the worst (largest) flaw among N flaws (where N is the number of
flaws in the specimen) determines the strength of a specimen; therefore, the theory of extreme values is applicable. Also, since N,
the number of flaws, is large, asymptotic theory is relevant.

    Griffith (5) first introduced the "largest flaw" concept (otherwise
known as the weakest-link hypothesis) to explain the much larger observed tensile strength of thin wires as compared with those of greater
diameter. Extending the principle of weakest-link theory, Weibull (19),
using heuristic arguments, derived the third asymptotic distribution of
smallest values and applied it to the analysis of breaking strength of
brittle solids. A formal derivation of the third asymptotic distribution can be seen in reference 9; the basic postulate that yields the
distribution is included here for ready reference.

    Let ξ_L be the random strength of a piece of material L with length
ℓ and suppose the material can be divided, at least hypothetically,
into smaller pieces, $L_1, \ldots, L_n$, of arbitrary lengths, $\ell_1, \ldots, \ell_n$, with
(random) strength, $\xi_{L_1}, \ldots, \xi_{L_n}$, respectively. We say that the material
is stochastically

    (i) *brittle*, if $\xi_L = \min(\xi_{L_1}, \ldots, \xi_{L_n})$,

(ii)   *homogeneous*, is the marginal distributions of $\xi_{L_1}, \ldots \xi_{L_n}$ depend on $\ell_1, \ldots, \ell_n$,

(iii) *disconnected*, if $\xi_{L_1}, \ldots, \xi_{L_n}$ are independent for all disjoint subdivisions $L_1, \ldots, L_n$ of L.

Of these properties, (ii) and (iii) are of purely statistical character, while (i) depends on the mechanism involved in a failure. All properties have definite physical meaning; and any specific material can, at least approximately, have one or more of the three properties.

Suppose a material satisfies (i)-(iii), and $F_\ell(\sigma)$ is the (nondegenerate) distribution function of the strength of a piece with length ℓ. Then

$$1 - F_1(\sigma) = \left(1 - F_{1/n}(\sigma)\right)^n \qquad (1)$$

Now, any d.f. $F_1(\sigma)$ satisfies Eq. 1 for some d.f. $F_{1/n}(\sigma)$, for example, $F_{1/n}(\sigma) = 1 - \left(1 - F_1(\sigma)\right)^{1/n}$. In order to obtain a simple structure for $F_1(\sigma)$, however, we introduce one additional restriction on the material: A material is called stochastically

(iv)   *size-stable*, if the distribution of ξ_1 is of the same type regardless of the length ℓ, i.e., there are constants $a_\ell > 0$, b_ℓ and a d.f. F, so that $F_\ell(\sigma) = F(a_\ell(\sigma - b_\ell))$.

This is an *ad hoc* notion but is frequently used in this context, since it leads to considerable mathematical simplification.

Thus strength distributions for materials satisfying (i)-(iv) are one of the three minimum extreme types. If, furthermore, the scale of measurement is such that the measured strength ξ_L is bounded below, $\xi_L \geq \sigma_u$ for some $\sigma_u \in (-\infty, \infty)$, then the only possibility is the Type III (or Weibull) distribution, with location parameter σ_u, and general scale parameter σ_o, i.e.,

$$F(\sigma) = 1 - \exp\left[-\left(\frac{\sigma - \sigma_u}{\sigma_o}\right)^m\right] \qquad , \qquad \sigma > \sigma_u \qquad (2)$$

for some constant m>0. Often $\sigma_u = 0$ is a natural choice, expressing the idea that strength can never be negative.

In addition, the d.f. $F^v(\sigma)$ of a piece with volume v can be shown to be,

$$F^v(\sigma) = 1 - \exp\left\{-\left(\frac{\sigma - \sigma_u}{\sigma_o}\right)^m v\right\} \qquad (3)$$

Note that Freudenthal (4) derived the same general expression from the logical assumption of fracture owing to largest cracks in the volume elements in conjunction with the weakest-link concept. How well the distribution function (Eq. 3) fits the failure data of stiff clays is examined in the next section.

Verification of the Weibull Theory/Size Effect

In order to validate the application of the Weibull theory, we analyzed data obtained from the carefully planned experimental program on stiff fissured London clay (11). The data in Fig. 1 (11, 2) clearly indicate that the shear strength of soils decreases with an increase in specimen diameter or size, which is one of the principal results of Weibull theory. An explicit relationship between sample size and shear strength is, therefore, sought to establish the applicability of Weibull theory to stiff clays.

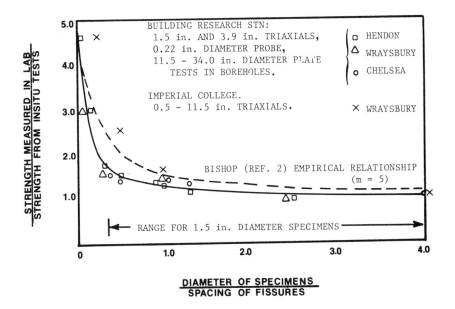

Fig. 1. Influence of the Ratio of Sample Size to the Fissure Spacing on the Strength Measured in Laboratory Tests. (1 in. = 25.4 mm) (after reference 11)

The strength distribution, Eq. 3, must be fulfilled if two specimens with different volumes are observed:

$$\left(\frac{\sigma_1 - \sigma_u}{\sigma_o}\right)^m v_1 = \left(\frac{\sigma_2 - \sigma_u}{\sigma_o}\right)^m v_2 \tag{4}$$

in which σ_1 = shear strength of specimen No. 1 of volume v_1; and σ_2 = shear strength of specimen No. 2 of volume v_2. Because for the same material both σ_o and m are the same, and σ_u could be neglected (since σ_u is nearly zero), a simple expression relating the shear strength to the corresponding volume is derived from Eq. 4:

$$\frac{\sigma_1}{\sigma_2} = \left(\frac{v_2}{v_1}\right)^{1/m} \tag{5}$$

Equation 5 clearly indicates that the larger the specimen, the weaker it is, provided that m is greater than 1.0. Also, it can be seen from Eq. 5 that the size effect increases as m (shape parameter) decreases. The shape parameter may be shown to be a material property closely related to the homogeneity of the material (soil), in that the smaller the variability in strength, the larger the m (1,7). The parameter m could also be viewed as a measure of flaw size uniformity or flaw dispersion; the more uniform the flaw size the larger the m. Some earlier studies support this conjecture; for example, m-values decrease in the order: for steel, m = 58 (14); for concrete m = 12 (21); and for soils m = 6 (as will be shown later). In other words, the size effect is less pronounced in homogeneous materials, for example, steel. In the following discussion, the authors, employing Marsland's shear strength data, attempt to estimate the parameter m for stiff fissured London clay.

Using the data in Fig. 1 (10), one can obtain a simple regression equation relating strength ratio to size of specimen:

$$\frac{\sigma}{\sigma_f} = 1.433\left(\frac{d}{\ell}\right)^{-0.334} \tag{6}$$

(with R^2 = 0.943;   SE = 0.180)

in which σ = laboratory shear strength of a specimen with diameter d and fissures spaced at ℓ; and σ_f = field shear strength. If σ_1 is the shear strength of specimen with diameter d_1, and σ_2 the shear strength of specimen corresponding to diameter d_2, Eq. 6, when expressed in terms of these parameters, results in the following:

$$\frac{\sigma_1}{\sigma_2} = \frac{\left(d_1/\ell_1\right)^{-0.334}}{\left(d_2/\ell_2\right)^{-0.334}} \tag{7}$$

Because the samples belong to the same deposit, the average spacing of fissures in the two samples, ℓ_1 and ℓ_2, is equal; accordingly, Eq. 7 becomes

$$\frac{\sigma_1}{\sigma_2} = \left(\frac{d_2}{d_1}\right)^{0.334} \tag{8}$$

In Eq. 5, diameters are substituted for volumes of specimens, and considering unit height, we obtain

$$\frac{\sigma_1}{\sigma_2} = \left(\frac{d_2}{d_1}\right)^{2/m} \tag{9}$$

Now the m-parameter of London clay is calculated by comparing Eqs. 8 and 9 (m = 6). A direct analysis of 64 shear strength values of a New York soft clay (12) resulted in a slightly lower value of 4.5 for m. These results serve only to indicate that parameter m for clays generally lies in the range of 4 to 6.

When the m-value of a clay, or any material for that matter, is known, the strength variability expressed by the coefficient of variation (CV) may be explicitly calculated. For example, Figure 3.3.8 of reference 1 may be used for this purpose. When m = 6, the CV for the stiff London clay is calculated to be 19.4%.

By virtue of the fact that stiff (overconsolidated) clay is fissured with numerous flaws in comparison to soft, normally consolidated clays, we conjectured that the former will show a larger scatter in the strength and, in turn, a smaller m-value. The shear strength results obtained by Simons (17) confirm this hypothesis in that the coefficient of variation of overconsolidated clay is approximately four percentage points larger than that for normally consolidated clay.

The question of which distribution better fits the shear strength is investigated by using the laboratory data on New York clay (12). Whether the observed frequencies differ significantly from frequencies expected from assumed models is tested by χ^2-test. The results, tabulated in Table 1 and graphed in Fig. 2, reveal that at the 5 percent level of significance, both normal and Weibull distributions fit the strength data, whereas the lognormal does not. The agreement between the normal and Weibull is coincidental because for values of the shape parameter m in the range 3.2<m<3.7, the Weibull probability function is very nearly symmetric and virtually indistinguishable from a normal distribution (4). Accordingly, the strength data of New York clay, having yielded an m-value of 4.5 for Weibull, might show good agreement with normal distribution, as can be verified in Fig. 2. With increasing values of m, however, one would expect the Weibull to deviate considerably from the normal distribution.

Since the proper selection of a d.f. for strength data is highly significant, we offer the following discussion to help identify the appropriate probability function in a given problem. In accordance with the central limit theorem (1), the lognormal distribution of a random variable results from combining several contributory factors by multiplication. Because theoreticl justification and/or experimental

data are lacking to show that strength of soils is governed by a set
of mutually independent variables that combine in a multiplicative
manner, we rule out the lognormal d.f. for soil strength. The question
now is whether a normal distribution would be appropriate for soil
strength. A discussion of this problem may be offered by postulating
an analytical model from the failure mechanism in clays. Experimental
evidence suggests that clays undergo great strain prior to failure.

Table 1. χ^2-test on Soft New York Clay; Mean Strength,
$\bar{\sigma}$ = 677 psf; Standard Deviation, S_σ= 173 psf.

Distribution Parameters	Degrees of Freedom	$\chi^2_{0.05}$	Normalized Squared Deviations, d^2
Normal	6	12.60	6.03
$\bar{\sigma}$ = 677 psf			
S_σ = 173 psf			
Weibull	5	11.30	4.82
m = 4.5			
σ_o = 752 psf			
σ_u = 0.0 psf			
Lognormal	6	12.60	15.20
$\bar{\sigma}$ = 677 psf			
S_σ = 0.251			

1 psf = 0.0478 kN/m^2

Strength distribution of materials failing in this manner has been obtained by applying the statistical theory of bundles of filaments after
Daniels and others (3, 6). Daniels has shown that, for a large number
of filaments, the distribution of strength of bundles of filaments
approaches a normal distribution. Extending this theory to bulk specimens using weakest-link statistics, one finds that the resulting distribution shows virtually no size effect. This result contradicts experimental findings on clayey soils including soft clays (12). Therefore,
the concept that led to the distribution function herein, namely, the
normal distribution, has questionable applicability in describing the
strength of clays. By a process of elimination and by virtue of the
fact that Weibull yields the best-fit curve in Fig. 2 (also, note that
it results in the smaller deviation in Table 1), one can assert that
the Weibull distribution represents a reasonable description of the soil
strength. The fact that this strength distribution belongs to one of
the three types of extreme value distribution for minima lends support
to this assertion.

The final verification process entails an analysis to determine
whether Weibull distribution can predict the characteristic size effect
exhibited by stiff clays. The triaxial strength data on 1.5 in. (38 mm)

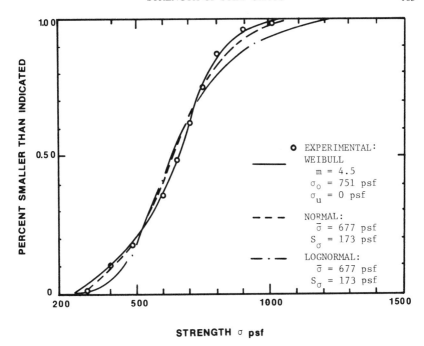

Fig. 2. Cumulative Distribution Function of Strength
(or Probability of Failure) of Soft New York
Clay (1 psf = 0.0478 kN/m²)

and 3.9 in. (98 mm) diameter samples are analyzed for this purpose (11).
Experimental data and the strength predicted by Eq. 9, with σ_u = 0 and
m = 6, are listed in columns 3 and 4, respectively, of Table 2. The
satisfactory agreement of the experimental data with the Weibull theory
may be considered as an empirical verification of the latter.

Significance of the Weibull Distribution in Safety Analysis

    As pointed out in an earlier section, strength parameters of clays
have been shown to follow a normal distribution (9, 15). The strength
data on New York clay tend to support this contention, despite the ob-
jection that a model conforming to this hypothesis fails to show size
effect. Another situation could arise wherein the data might apparently
fit a normal distribution; but, in reality, a Weibull d.f. with shape
parameter in the nieghborhood of 3.5 would be the appropriate relation.
The question, therefore, is what if the strength of stiff fissured clay
is represented by a normal distribution instead of the Weibull. The

Table 2.   Comparison of the Experimentally Measured Shear
           Strength of London Clay (11) and the Shear Strength
           Predicted by Eq. 9.

Effective Stress, σ', psf	Shear Strength of specimen, σ_2 (Diameter d_2 = 3.9 in.) psf	Shear Strength of specimen, σ_1 (Diameter d_1 = 1.5 in.) psf	
		Experiment	Using Eq. 9 with m = 6
1879	877	1337	1203
2088	940	1408	1288
2297	1044	1479	1434
2506	1149	1552	1574
2715	1211	1629	1662

1 in. = 2.54 cm
1 psf = 0.0478 kN/m^2

question of whether such a choice will result in an unsafe design is
examined in a safety analysis of stiff fissured London clay. The following properties are adapted from Marsland's test data.

Shear strength corresponding to a normal
  stress of 9,576 psf (200 kN/m^2)   : 2160 psf (103 kN/m^2)
  (Fig. 1-38, reference 11)

Weibull shape parameter, m, evaluated in
  the preceding section   : 6

Corresponding coefficient of variation   : 19.4%
  (Fig. 3.3.8, reference 1)

Standard deviation   : 419 psf (20 kN/m^2)

Using these soil parameters, the authors list in Table 3 the estimated
maximum stresses (load) allowable for a wide range of failure rates.

Table 3.   Allowable Stresses in Accordance with
           Assumed Strength Distributions.

Failure Rate (Probability of Failure)	Maximum Allowable Stress, psf, In Accordance with	
	Weibull	Normal
1 in 100	1,081	1,188
1 in 1,000	736	865
1 in 10,000	501	601

1 psf = 0.0478 kN/m^2

The above results clearly demonstrate that for stiff fissured London clay, adopting a Weibull distribution for strength (m = 6), results in prediction of a smaller allowable stress, which in turn yields a conservative design. It should be pointed out that the discrepancy in allowable loads tends to increase with an increase in the shape parameter. These results emphasize the importance of selecting an appropriate d.f. in probabilistic safety analysis of fissured-clay structures.

Summary and Conclusions

The statistical approach to failure of stiff clays is concerned with two problems: the distribution function of strength of nominally identical specimens under nominally identical conditions, and the effect on strength of specimen size. These problems are interrelated, and their solution requires the construction of plausible physical-statistical models of the failure process.

Postulating a defect structure for stiff fissured clays, the authors have identified an extreme value distribution for minima (Weibull d.f.) and validated it by using the shear strength data of stiff fissured London clay. Size effect exhibited by London clay is also substantiated by the Weibull function. In estimating the most probably minimum strength of stiff clays for safety analysis, Weibull d.f., because of its emphasis on defect structure, is favored over the normal or lognormal distributions. A comparative analysis of the adequacy of the distributions reveals that Weibull d.f. gives rise to relatively conservative design in fissured clays.

Acknowledgment

The importance of scale problems in engineering was brought to the authors' attention by Professor V. K. Gupta, who enthusiastically supported this investigation by making helpful comments throughout the study. The guidance of Professor Gupta is gratefully acknowledged. This work was partly supported by the funds from the Civil Engineering Department.

Appendix - References

1. Benjamin, J. R. and Cornell, C. A., Probability, Statistics, and Decision for Civil Engineers, 1st ed., McGraw Hill, New York, N.Y., 1970, pp. 271-285.

2. Bishop, A. W., Discussion, "Progressive Failure with Special Reference to the Mechanism Causing It," Proceedings, Geotechnical Conference, Vol. 2, Oslo, 1967.

3. Daniels, H. E., Proceedings, The Royal Society of London, Vol. A183, 1945, pp. 405-435.

4. Freudenthal, A. M., "Statistical Approach to Brittle Fracture," Fracture: An Advanced Treatise, (edited by H. Liebowitz), Vol. II, 1968, pp. 591-618.

5. Griffith, A. A., "The Phenomena of Rupture and Flow in Solids," Philosophical Transactions of the Royal Society of London, Vol. A221, 1920, pp. 163-198.

6. Gücer, D. E. and Gurland, J., "Comparison of the Statistics of Two Fracture Models," Journal of Mechanics and Solids, Vol. 10, 1962, pp. 365-373.

7. Harlow, D. G. and Phoenix, S. L., "Bounds on the Probability of Failure of Composite Materials," International Journal of Fracture, Vol. 15, No. 4, 1979, pp. 321-336.

8. Karmarsch, K., "Ueber die absolute Festigkeit der Metalldrahte," Mittheilungen des Gewerbe-Vereins fur Hanover, Vol. 3, 1859, pp. 137-156.

9. Leadbetter, M. R., Lindgren, G. and Rootzen, H., Extremes and Related Properties of Random Sequences and Processes, Springer-Verlag, 1983, pp. 267-277.

10. Lumb, P., "Variability of Natural Soils," Canadian Geotechnical Journal, Vol. 3, No. 2, May 1966.

11. Marsland, A., "The Shear Strength of Stiff Fissured Clays," Proceedings, The Roscoe Memorial Symposium, Cambridge, England, 1971, pp. 59-68.

12. McGuffey, V., Iori, J., Kyfor, Z., and Athanasiou-Gravas, D., "Statistical Geotechnical Properties of Lockport Clays," Transportation Research Board Record 809, 1980, pp. 54-60.

13. Meyerhof, G. G., "Scale Effects of Ultimate Pile Capacity," Journal of the Geotechnical Engineering Divsion, ASCE, Vol. 109, No. 6, June 1983, pp. 797-806.

14. Richards, C. W., "Size Effect in the Tension Test of Mild Steel," Proceedings, ASTM, Vol. 54, 1954, pp. 995-1002.

15. Rowe, P. W., "Progressive Failure and Strength of a Sand Mass," Proceedings, Seventh International Conference on Soil Mechanics and Foundation Engineering, Vol. 1, 1969, pp. 341-349.

16. Schultze, E., "Frequency Distributions and Correlations of Soil Properties," Statistics and Probability in Civil Engineering, Hong Kong University Press, distributed by Oxford University Press, London, 1972.

17. Simons, N. E., "The Effect of Overconsolidation on the Shear Strength Characteristics of an Undisturbed Oslo Clay," Research Conference on Shear Strength of Cohesive Soils, ASCE, June 1960, pp. 747-763.

18. Skempton, A. W., "Summing Up," Proceedings, Symposium on Large Bored Piles, Institution of Civil Engineers, London, England, 1960, pp. 155-157.

STRENGTH OF STIFF CLAYS 169

19. Weibull, W., "A Statistical Theory of the Strength of Materials," Ingeniors Vetenskaps Akademien Handlinger, No. 1951, 1939, Stockholm.

20. Whitaker, T., and Cooke, R. W., "An Investigation of the Shaft and Resistance of Large Bored Piles in London Clay," Proceedings, Symposium on Large Bored Piles, Institution of Civil Engineers, London, England, pp. 7-49.

21. Zech, B. and Wittman, F. H., "Probabilistic Approach to Describe the Behavior of Materials," Transaction of the Fourth International Conference on Structural Mechanics in Reactor Technology, 1977, pp. 575-584.

LANDFORM-BASED CHARACTERIZATION OF SOIL PROPERTIES

Charles L. Vita[1], M. ASCE

ABSTRACT

Site characterization where site-specific borehole and associated test data are relatively sparse (or even unavailable) is a common situation in geotechnical engineering practice. If the landforms occurring at the site can be identified (by airphoto interpretation and/or field reconnaissance), the field and laboratory results of past exploration programs conducted in or partly in other regional occurrences of the landforms identified at the site can be used with the available site-specific data to provide an increased data base from which improved, "updated" estimates of site-specific geotechnical property parameters can be made. Where relatively large landform data bases can be developed by organizing and statistically characterizing available field and associated laboratory data for a given region on a landform basis, Bayesian probability procedures can be used to supplement/augment site-specific data. These procedures can systematize the input of pertinent "past experience" into the site characterization process on a consistent and rational site-specific basis. The conceptual basis and an example application of this landform-based methodology is presented.

INTRODUCTION

A probabilistic characterization of site soil properties can be achieved with sparse site-specific data by augmenting them with data available from other sites in the region having the same geologically characteristic landform. This is generally appropriate for site characterizations in large regions where landforms have been (or can be) mapped and adequate data are available for landform geotechnical property characterizations but site-specific data are (typically) locally sparse. Site soil properties can be used in making probabilistic predictions of geotechnical behavior useful to facility planning, analysis, or design. In particular, transportation routes traversing complex terrain can provide an excellent opportunity for application which can be used in an overall systems approach to planning, analysis and design [11,12].

This paper summarizes important concepts of landform characterization, presents pertinent updating equations, discusses soil profile development, and includes an illustrative, site-specific application of the method.

[1] Vice President, R&M Consultants, Inc., 18539 NE 184th Street, Woodinville, WA 98072

LANDFORM CHARACTERIZATION

Landforms are elements of the landscape formed by a single geologic process or a combination of associated processes which have both characteristic surface forms (such as topography, drainage patterns and gully morphology) and typical, recurrent ranges of geotechnical properties, including characteristic distributions of soil properties, such as density, moisture and grain sizes. Sand dunes, moraines, floodplains, alluvial fans, and glaciofluvial outwash are all examples of landforms. Each have characteristic surface forms that can be identified by field observation and airphoto or other remote sensing interpretation techniques [13].

Once the landforms at a site are identified, the characteristic distributions of landform soil properties (as well as some understanding of stratigraphy, soil structure, drainage characteristics, and groundwater conditions) can be inferred. The sharper the distributions the more precisely can geotechnical properties and behavior be predicted. Sharp distributions are associated with uniform or "homogeneous" properties and broad distributions with variable or "heterogeneous" properties. A given landform can have either homogeneous or heterogeneous properties, or both. For example, sand dunes are relatively homogeneous in all properties, glacial tills relatively heterogeneous in most properties, and landforms composed of wind blown silts may have a homogeneous grain size distribution but heterogeneous moisture content. Distributions of geotechnical properties are variable with landform location because of differences in climate, weathering rates and processes, and predominant bedrock type. Landform property distributions are also sample volume (site size) dependent; uniformity or homogeneity between samples or "sites" tends to increase with sample volume (site size) depending on the degree of spatial autocorrelation of the property (e.g., see "Krige's relation" [4]).

DATA SOURCES.--Landform geotechnical property distributions are determined from data obtained primarily from field boring, trenching, sampling and testing programs and from laboratory testing of representative soil samples recovered from field exploration programs. Geologic field observations of road cuts, material pits, and naturally exposed surfaces also add to the understanding of landform properties. Basic understandings come from interpretation of the geologic processes themselves.

Landform property parameters must be interpreted and characterized with proper engineering and geologic appreciation of potential data bias effects. Biased data effects can come about in several major ways: (1) borehole location selection, (2) noncontinuous sampling and testing, (3) sampling disturbance, and (4) sample size limitations and associated testing effects. Biases of the first kind include both random and systematic effects; the latter occurs where borehole programs select for non-representative problem conditions. The second source of bias tends to be random over the landform, and can cancel out for large numbers of samples; it can also be treated by geologically interpolating/extrapolating the characteristics of recovered samples to the observed strata. The third and fourth kinds of bias tend to be systematic; e.g., in sampling coarse grained soils, soil structure can be disturbed, dense soil loosened, loose soil densified, and soil sizes coarser than a fraction of the sampler's apperture not recovered--erroneously skewing grain size distributions to smaller fractions. Sampling and testing biases should be controlled and any skewing affects on geotechnical parameters or interpretations adequately rectified.

GEOGRAPHIC SCALES AND UPDATING.--Landform data for site characterization are available at three (or more) geographic scales. In order of decreasing size and data availability but increasing geographic specificity these are (1) for all known occurrences of a landform or landform group (of similar landforms), (2) for all regional occurrences of a landform or landform group within a particular local geologic region, unit or physiographic province and (3) for site-specific occurrences of the landform in the given region. The site-specific scale can be subdivided as desired to the meaningful limit supported by available data. Note that the data comprising the property distributions for each geographic scale are made up of the collective data of the geographically smaller scale(s).

In general, landform property distributions are scale and location dependent. It is assumed that the forms of the probability density functions (PDF) or basic shapes of the property distributions are constant, whereas the statistical parameters of the PDFs generally are location and scale dependent [9,12]. Landform property parameters that are not strongly location dependent for a given site size (volume) are "statistically homogeneous;" parameters that are relatively location dependent are "statistically heterogeneous." Statistical homogeneity implies site-to-site uniformity; conversely, statistical heterogeneity implies site-to-site variability. Statistical homogeneity (between sites) tends to increase with site size [4].

The working principal for predicting landform soil properties wherever the landform occurs is to utilize all available representative data obtained for the given landform. Combining landform data from different geographic scales and locations is termed "geographical updating." Incorporating additional, new information at a given geographic scale or location is termed "informational updating". Both forms of updating utilize Bayesian techniques [9,12].

Geographical updating proceeds down the level of scale in the direction of increasing site specificity. Data for each landform (or landform group) are (1) combined to form a set of landform statistics, and (2) separated by geologic region to form a set of landform-/regional statistics. The landform/regional statistics can be used to update the landform statistics to produce posterior, or updated, estimates of the parameters of the property distribution of the landform-/region. These can be used as prior data for site-specific occurrences of the landform and used with site-specific sample data to calculate posterior, updated estimates of the parameters of the property distributions for each stratum comprising a site soil profile. Geographical updating can be accomplished at consecutively greater levels of site-specificity, if data availability and needs warrant it; the principals of updating apply in the same way. With time, as more data become available, each scale can itself be informationally updated to reflect the new data.

PROBABILISTIC (BAYESIAN) UPDATING

Geographic and informational updating are based on Bayesian statistical techniques [2] where the variability in the property(s) of
interest, X (material and/or geometric), is describable by a known
probability density function, PDF[X] having uncertain mean and vari-
ance parameters, θ. Uncertainty in θ is described by PDF[θ]. Subject-
/site-specific estimates of θ, $\theta(S)$, are made using prior data and
available subject/site-specific sample data to make posterior, updated
estimates of $\theta(S)$, $\theta(S)$", as follows: Subject/site-specific parameters
$\theta(S)$ are random variables (in the Bayesian sense) having prior distributions PDF[$\theta(S)$]' based on available prior data on X. Subject/site-
specific sample data on property X, x(S), are summarized by a sample
likelihood function, L[$\theta(S)/x(S)$], which gives the relative likeli-
hoods of the uncertain values of $\theta(S)$ given x(S). Using Bayes' rule
the posterior, updated PDF of $\theta(S)$, PDF[$\theta(S)$]", is equal to the product of PDF[$\theta(S)$]' and L[$\theta(S)/x(S)$], and normalized so PDF[$\theta(S)$]" inte-
grates to unity [2]. The updated statistical parameters mean,
E[$\theta(S)$]", and variance, Var[$\theta(S)$]", follow from PDF[θ]".

Table 1 presents the pertinent mathematics [7,9,12] of two particularly useful conjugate pair PDF models: a normal model and a binomial model. For example, observed PDF[X]s for soil density, moisture content, shear strength parameters, and compressibility parameters tend to follow bell shaped Beta distributions [3,6]. The central
portions of the Beta distributions can be described by normal [5,6]
and lognormal or inverse lognormal distributions (by simple log-
arithmic transformations the latter two distributions can be transformed into normal distributions). Thus, practical updating of bell
shaped distributions of any soil property X (subsequent to suitable
transformation if necessary) can be done assuming PDF[X] is normal
(defined by the two parameters mean of X, $\overline{X}$, and standard deviation of
X,σ) and using the normal PDF model updating equations given in Table
1. Also, the soil property parameter of interest in grain size characterizations is commonly associated with the proportion, u, compared
to a critical value, U, of a soil which is finer than a specified
grain size (gravel, sand, silt, clay, or any particular grain size
fraction). The probability of the number, Z, of fundamentally sized,
effectively homogeneous soil volumes composing a site (or stratum) of
volume V and having u<U can be modelled by the binomial distribution.
The number of effective soil volumes comprising V is the effective
number of trials, n, so that Q, the estimated probability that u<U in
any effective soil volume can be estimated using the binomial PDF
model updating equations presented in Table 1. Proper application of
these techniques requires judgment and understanding of their applica-
tion-specific limitations.

Using landform prior data to augment subject/site-specific sample
date requires that a weight (n') be assigned to the landform data. In
all cases the subject/site-specific data are weighted by the available
(subject/site-specific) sample size, n. Establishing suitable values
for n' requires geotechnical judgment; it is discussed below in the
illustrative application and in mathematical detail in reference [12].

Assumed Soil Property PDF Model and Uncertain Parameters of Model	Prior and Posterior PDF of Parameters	Updated Estimates of Mean and Variance of Parameters for Site	
NORMAL. With uncertain parameters: mean, $\bar{X}$, and standard deviation, σ, of property X $$PDF'(X) = \frac{1}{\sqrt{2\pi}\sigma} \exp[-\tfrac{1}{2}(\tfrac{X-\bar{X}}{\sigma})^2]$$	STUDENT, INVERTED-GAMMA-2 $$PDF'(\bar{X}) = \{(n-1)^{\frac{1}{2}n-\frac{1}{2}} \cdot \frac{s/\sqrt{n}}{\sqrt{\pi}} \cdot \frac{\Gamma[n/2]}{\Gamma[\frac{1}{2}n-\frac{1}{2}]}$$ $$\cdot [n-1+n\cdot(\bar{X}-\bar{x})^2/s^2]^{-\frac{1}{2}n}\}$$	$E[\bar{X}(S)]'' = \bar{x}'' = \dfrac{n'\cdot\bar{x}(Lf)+n\cdot\bar{x}(S)}{n'+n}$	(I.1)
		$Var[\bar{X}(S)]'' = \dfrac{s''^2(n'+n-1)}{(n'+n)\cdot(n'+n-3)}$	(I.2)
		$E[\sigma^2(S)]'' = \dfrac{s''^2\cdot(n'+n-1)}{(n'+n-3)}$	(I.3)
	$PDF'(\sigma) = \{\dfrac{2(\frac{1}{2}n-\frac{1}{2})^{\frac{1}{2}n-\frac{1}{2}}}{s\cdot\Gamma[\frac{1}{2}n-\frac{1}{2}]} \cdot (\dfrac{s^2}{\sigma^2})^{\frac{1}{2}n}\}$ $\cdot \exp[-\tfrac{1}{2}(n-1)s^2/\sigma^2]\}$	$E[\sigma(S)]'' = \sqrt{\dfrac{s''^2\cdot(n'+n-1)}{2}} \cdot \dfrac{\Gamma[(n'+n-2)/2]}{\Gamma[(n'+n-1)/2]}$	(I.4)
	$PDF'': \bar{x}=\bar{x}(Lf), \ s^2=s(Lf)^2, \ n=n'$	$Var[\sigma(S)]'' = E[\sigma^2(S)]'' - E^2[\sigma(S)]''$	(I.5)
	$PDF'': \bar{x}=\bar{x}'', \ s^2=s''^2, \ n=n''$ $$s''^2=[(n-1)\cdot s(S)^2+(n'-1)\cdot s(Lf)^2$$ $$+n'\cdot n\cdot[\bar{x}(Lf)-\bar{x}(S)]^2/n+2]$$ $$(n'+n-1)$$		
BINOMIAL. With uncertain parameter: the probability, Q, property u is below a critical value U $$PDF'(Z)=\binom{\eta}{z}Q^z(1-Q)^{\eta-z}$$	BETA $$PDF'(Q) = \frac{\Gamma(\alpha+\beta)}{\Gamma(\alpha)\cdot\Gamma(\beta)} Q^{\alpha-1} (1-Q)^{\beta-1}$$ $\alpha=n\cdot Q(Lf)+n\cdot Q(S)+1$ $\beta=n\cdot[1-Q(Lf)]+n\cdot[1-Q(S)]+1$	$E[Q(S)]'' = \dfrac{n'\cdot Q(Lf)+n\cdot Q(S)+1}{n'+n+2}$	(II.1)
		$Var[Q(S)]'' = E[Q(S)]''\cdot\left[\dfrac{1-E[Q(S)]''}{n'+n+3}\right]$	(II.2)

$\bar{x}(Lf), s(Lf)^2$ = sample mean and variance of landform (or any) prior

$\bar{x}(S), s(S)^2$ = sample mean and variance of site

$Q(Lf)$ = Estimated probability u<U based on landform data

$Q(S)$ = Estimated probability u<U based on site data

(Lf) identifies information from landform (or any) prior

(S) identifies site-specific information

n' = landform (or any) prior sample weight; n = site sample weight

n" = n'+n = posterior sample weight

TABLE 1.--UPDATING EQUATIONS FOR SOIL PROPERTY PARAMETER ESTIMATING

If n' is adequate, estimates of $\theta(S)$ can be made with any amount of site-specific data (n)--including no data (n=0). Uncertainty in all estimates, measured by $Var[\theta(S)]"$, decreases with increasing site-specific data (increasing n).

SOIL PROFILE DEVELOPMENT

Soil profiles are engineering constructs used to idealize soil stratigraphy and associated material properties within a specific site area for engineering analysis and design purposes. Conceptually, soil profile development starts with identification of the landform profiles (geologic cross sections of the landforms) at the site, which are then refined as needed using available site-specific data. Each point of a site can belong to more than one soil profile if significantly different characterizations are required for the various specific analysis and design purposes--e.g., within the limits of available data, site soil profiles characterized for slope/ embankment stability may be different than soil profiles characterized for settlement, frost heave, bearing capacity, or erosion, etc.

OBJECTIVE.--The primary objective of soil profile development is to adequately represent--as simply as possible--the pertinent geological and geotechnical details that could potentially affect the conditions or structures of concern. Soil profile detail has practical meaning only if it influences geotechnical behavior and facility performance; unnecessary details include refinements beyond the resolution of analysis or judgment to predict meaningful differences in geotechnical responses or, moreover, refinements which either do not or could not affect design. Structures sensitive to geotechnical behavior tend to need more accurate soil profiles than less sensitive structures, for a given level of acceptable risk (the trade-offs are between conservative design and greater exploration and analysis).

Differences between landform profiles (representing spatial relationships of soils having similar geological genesis) and soil profiles are dependent on anticipated engineering behavior. Landform changes affect soil profiles where the changes potentially affect geotechnical response. Contiguous landforms may have sufficiently similar engineering characteristics that they can be treated as a single stratum or soil profile. Or, a single landform may be characterized by more than one stratum because of significant spatial differences in soil property parameters within the occurrence of the landform at that site. Thus, soil profiles can be simplifications or elaborations of landform profiles.

UPDATING OF SOIL PROFILES.--Soil property parameters for each stratum in the soil profile are estimated using available site-specific (sample) data and statistically characterized landform (prior) information. Soil profile strata should be locally statistically homogeneous; i.e., within a given stratum the mean and variance of the pertinent soil property parameters should not be significantly depth or location dependent. Soil profiles can be discretized or standardized so that all strata are reasonably statistically homogeneous (within limitations of available data). Soil profile development can be an iterative process with successive refinement of the soil profile ge-

ometry and parameter estimates. For each stratum all pertinent geotechnical property statistical parameters are characterized by an
updated estimate of their mean and variance. The updated soil profile
can be used directly in subsequent analysis and design [10,12]. If
necessary, updated parameters can be used to characterize geotechnical
property probability distributions with a Beta PDF (to keep probabilistic extremes to physically realistic limits).

     Soil profiles having landforms characteristically composed of sig-
nificantly different soil types (e.g., heterogeneous tills) could
utilize soil type-dependent landform (prior) parameters with updated
site-specific estimates conditioned on observed soil types. Also,
updated site-specific estimates for soil profiles where landforms are
uncertain and/or occur in complex associations can be made by condi-
tioning estimates on the expected probability of occurrence of the
various potential conditions (the sensitivity of such estimates to the
uncertainty, particularly the potential extreme conditions, should be
evaluated). For such cases landform prior statistics would be developed as a function of selected soil types (e.g., predominant soil
grain size distribution) and corresponding stratigraphic parameters
(e.g., frequency of occurrence and spatial characteristics). Selection
criteria for the chosen soil type categories should consider (1) com-
patibility with available field log stratigraphic data and soil descriptions, (2) geotechnical predictive value, and (3) available sample sizes. Stratigraphic prior statistics can be used to help guide
soil profile stratigraphic characterization; soil property prior information, by selected soil type, can be used with the site-specific
data to estimate soil property parameters for each stratum.

LIMITATIONS ON INTERPRETATIONS.--Conservative compensation for data
limitations in soil profile development may be limited to emphasizing
potentially critical stratigraphic details. For example, with only
one borehole at a site a single thin low density silt "stratum" observed in otherwise medium density granular soils could be a local
lens but, unless there was sufficient geological reason to preclude
the possibility, may be identified as the critical slope stability
stratum if it could potentially control the stability of the site. If
cost-effective, more borehole data could be obtained to determine the
actual extent of the silt zone.

     Without site-specific subsurface data soil profiles are limited
to inferred landform profiles and a prior knowledge of characteristic
landform stratigraphy and associated material properties. Interpretation of the geotechnical response of the profile could statistically
consider the potential effects of the characteristic stratigraphy and
properties. This could be useful in preliminary siting studies, prior
to site-specific subsurface exploration.

     Available site data are typically too sparse to support meaning-
ful probabilistic autocorrelation characterizations of soil and rock
strata (although it has been suggested [8], but not demonstrated, that
autocorrelation effects may not be site-dependent for similar soil
types). The mathematical theory used here ignores autocorrelation
effects. However, the potential practical importance of autocorrelation effects should be evaluated application-specifically and site-

specifically--particularly the potential influence of autocorrelation on biasing the mean and underestimating the variance of soil property estimates.

Development of the site soil profile is dependent on site geology and limited by available site data. Erratic soil profiles are the most difficult to characterize; they require greater geologic insight into the processes involved in formation of the site. Depending on the design phase, adequate consideration must be given to the impact of very localized geological inhomogeneities which can dominate engineering behavior; such geological details can be spatially complex, interdependent (e.g., past failure surfaces, ground ice in permafrost, solution cavities in limestone, etc.) and easy to miss because of limited data. The potential effect of unanticipated negative conditions should be considered since, regardless of specific technique, subsurface conditions are never completely defined in exploration or analysis--such that critical geotechnical details may go undetected or be inadequately interpreted and eventually results in unsatisfactory performance. Careful engineering and geological interpretations and assumptions based on sound judgment remains fundamental to the site characterization process [1].

ILLUSTRATIVE APPLICATION

The average frozen dry density over a critical stratum of a site, $\bar{\gamma}_{df}(S)$, is estimated using landform prior data to augment available site-specific data. Estimates of $\bar{\gamma}_{df}(S)$ have been systematically correlated using regression analysis with thawed soil shear strength parameters and thaw strain potential and used with Taylor series expansion techniques to probabilistically evaluate thawing slope stability and thaw settlement [10]. Because the observed PDF[γ_{df}] adequately resembles a normal distribution, using from Table 1 Eqs I.1 and I.2 (with $n'=w$), the updated landform/site data estimates of the mean and variance of $\bar{\gamma}_{df}(S)$ are:

$$E\left[\bar{\gamma}_{df}(S)\right]'' = \frac{\bar{x}(S)\cdot n + \bar{x}(Lf)\cdot w}{n + w} \tag{1}$$

$$Var\left[\bar{\gamma}_{df}(S)\right]'' = \frac{(n-1)\cdot s(S)^2 + (w-1)\cdot s(Lf)^2 + n\cdot w\cdot\left[\bar{x}(Lf)-\bar{x}(S)\right]^2/(n+2)}{(w+n)\cdot(w+n-3)} \tag{2}$$

where: n is the number of available samples from the site; $\bar{x}(S)$, $s(S)^2$ and $\bar{x}(Lf)$, $s(Lf)^2$ are the sample mean and variance of the site and landform γ_{df} data respectively; w is calculated from Equation 3 where N is the number of samples from the landform and α is the estimated ratio of Var[$\gamma_{df}(Lf)$] to the variance of the observed distribution of E[$\bar{\gamma}_{df}(S)$] for all other sites in the subject landform [12].

$$\left(\frac{N-3}{N-1}\right) \cdot \frac{(w+n-1)}{(w+n) \cdot (w+n-3)} = \frac{1}{\alpha+n} \qquad (3)$$

In general, α is a random variable ($\alpha > 1$) estimated from prior data and dependent on (1) site size (ranging from 1.0 for sample-sized "sites" to $\sqrt{N}$ for a landform-sized site); (2) landform geological/statistical characteristics ($\alpha=1$ reflects greatest site-to-site variability, α being relatively larger for statistically homogeneous landforms); and (3) the quality, quantity, and statistical uncertainty of available prior site data ($\alpha=1$ reflects least admissible quallity, quantity or greatest uncertainty).

Site data-based estimates are made (utilizing site-specific data only) by neglecting landform prior data and letting $\alpha=w=0$. Note that Equation 2 is undefined for site data-based estimates where $n<4$; the assumption that $\bar{\gamma}_{df}(S)$ is uniformly distributed over a maximum possible range R introduces the least possible bias and gives $Var[\bar{\gamma}_{df}(S)]=R^2/12$, centered at $\bar{x}(S)$, which is at least as conservative as is the estimate of R. In this example R=1,100 (70 pcf), 800 (50 pcf), and 640 (40 pcf) kg/m^3 for n=1, 2 and 3, respectively. Site data-based estimated are compared with updated estimates using landform prior data.

RESULTS.--Fig 1 displays specific results for a several-acre permafrost site located in a landform composed of colluvial silt. Results are plotted as a function of the estimated expected value, $E[\bar{\gamma}_{df}]$, and estimated standard deviation, $SD[\bar{\gamma}_{df}]$, of the (uncertain) average frozen dry density of the critical statum, $\bar{\gamma}_{df}(S)$.

Two cases are illustrated in Fig 1. Case 1 shows sample-by-sample results for a site-specific stratum that is similar to the landform as a whole, i.e., $\bar{\gamma}_{df}(S) \approx \bar{\gamma}_{df}(Lf)$. Case 1 shows actual site data with $\alpha=3$, representing a relatively statistically homogeneous landform. Both updated landform/site data estimates ($\alpha > 1$) and site data-based estimates ($\alpha=w=0$) are shown (the numbers next to box and circle symbols on case study results indicate number of samples from the site, n). Case 2 shows actual sample γ_{df} data reduced by 320 kg/m^2 (20 pcf) with $\alpha=1$, representing a statistically variable landform or one where either little information on other sites is available or it is of poor quality such that a minimum α is considered prudent. Case 2 simulates sample-by-sample results for a site-specific stratum that is substantially less dense than the landform as a whole, i.e., $\bar{\gamma}_{df}(S) << \bar{\gamma}_{df}(Lf)$. A total of n=40 samples (each from one borehole) were obtained from the critical stratum. Sample-by-sample results for the first 10 (n=1,2,...10) samples are plotted; results based on all 40 samples are given for comparison.

This same site and $\gamma_{df}(S)$ data was probabilistically evaluated by Vita [10] for slope stability factor of safety (FS) and thaw settlement (TS). In Fig 2 results of these analyses are superimposed on Fig 1; contours are shown of the mean of TS, $E[TS]$, coefficient of variation of TS, $CV[TS]$, the mean of FS, $E[FS]$, stability margin U, $U=(E[FS]-1)/SD[FS]$, and estimated probability of slope instability Pf,

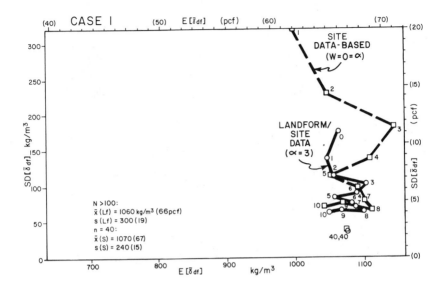

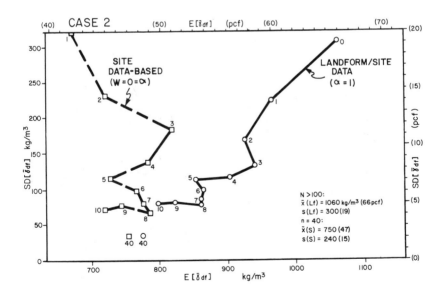

FIG 1.--SITE-SPECIFIC RESULTS FOR ILLUSTRATIVE APPLICATION

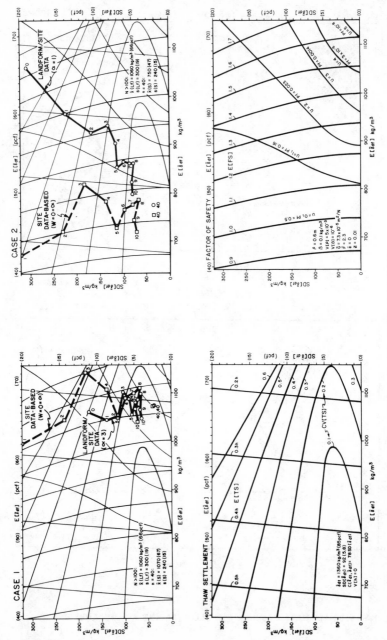

FIG 2.--SITE-SPECIFIC RESULTS, THAW SETTLEMENT AND SLOPE STABILITY.

the probability FS<1.0 (assuming FS normally distributed between 1.0 and E[FS]).

Case 1 (actual γ_{df} data) shows the efficiency of the updated landform/site data method when the site is in fact similar to the landform: uncertainty in all estimates is significantly reduced at small n relative to the site data-based estimate. Case 2 simulates the effect of a statistically unlikely or "negative surprise" site--one that is in fact much less dense (and therefore less stable) than the landform as a whole. The benefits of the updated landform/site data method for Case 2 sites are derived through comparison with the site data-based predictions: at small n potentially significant differences become obvious--suggesting the potential need for further exploration, analysis, or changed design.

SUMMARY AND CONCLUSIONS

As outlined here, the landform-based probabilistic approach can be systematically used within and through all levels and phases of the planning and design process. As examples, it could be used (1) in project planning at the feasibility or site selection stages to quantitatively identify, at selected confidence levels and consistent with data availability, the geotechnical characteristics of candidate sites; (2) in preliminary or final exploration planning to estimate and set levels of needed effort: more to heterogeneous and problem sites, less to homogenous and nonproblem sites; and (3) in preliminary and final analysis and design, by augmenting site-specific data, to increase the information otherwise available for site characterization. In general, the quantity of site-specific data required to achieve a given safety margin increases as the statistical heterogenity of the landform increases. For all sites the quantity of site-specific data required for a given purpose varies directly with the desired safety margin or degree of certitude. In all cases, as the amount of site-specific data increases the influence and value of the landform (prior data) decreases. For any specific application, the usefulness of the approach is dependent on the pertinent landform characteristics, data availability and desired safety margin of the predictions.

APPENDIX I.--REFERENCES

1. Baecher, G.B., "Exploration Strategies", Proceedings, Site Characterization & Exploration, ASCE, June, 1978

2. Benjamin, Jack R. and Cornell, Allen C., Probability, Statistics, and Decision for Civil Engineers, McGraw-Hill, New York, 1970.

3. Harr, M.E., Mechanics of Particulate Media - A Probabilistic Approach, McGraw-Hill, 1977.

4. Journel, A.G. and Huijbregts, Ch., J., Mining Geostatistics, Academic Press, New York, 1978.

5. Lumb, P., "Variability of Natural Soils," Canadian Geotechnical Journal, Vol. 7, No. 3, 1970.

6. Lumb, P., "Safety Factors and Probability Distribution of Soil Strength," Canadian Geotechnical Journal, Vol. 7, No. 3, 1970.

7. Raiffa, H. and Schlaifer, R., Applied Statistical Decision Theory, Harvard University Press, Cambridge, MA., 1961

8. Vanmarke, Erik H., "Probabilistic Characterization of Soil Profiles" Proceedings Site Characterization & Exploration, ASCE, June, 1978.

9. Vita, Charles L., "A Landform-Based Probabilistic Methodology for Site Characterization," Proceedings Nineteenth Annual Symposium on Engineering Geology and Soils Engineering, Idaho State University, April, 1982.

10. _____, "Thaw Plug Stability and Thaw Settlement Evaluation for Arctic Transportation Routes: A Probabilistic Approach," Proceedings, Permafrost: Fourth International Conference, National Academy Press, Washington D. C., July, 1983.

11. _____, "A Geotechnical Engineering Systems Approach For Arctic Transportation Facility Planning and Design," Civil Engineering Systems, England, Vol. 1, No. 2, Dec. 1983.

12. _____, "Route Geotechnical Characterization and Analysis," accepted for publication, Journal of Geotechnical Engineering, ASCE, forthcoming.

13. Way, Douglas, Terrain Analysis, 2nd Ed., McGraw-Hill, New York, 1978.

SUBJECT INDEX
Page number refers to first page of paper.

AUTHOR INDEX
Page number refers to first page of paper.